Wave properties

Advanced Physics Project for Independent Learning

Student's Guide

John Murray
in association with
Inner London Education Authority

How to use this student's guide

This is a programme for independent learning. It is not a textbook: it is a guide to using texts, experiments and other resources to help you to learn about waves.

Objectives

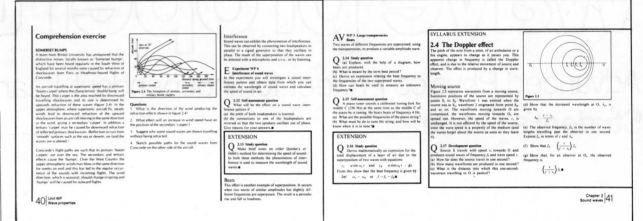

What is to be learnt is stated at the beginning of each chapter — a general statement of what you will be doing, and more detailed objectives to be achieved. The *objectives* are particularly important, because they tell you what you should be able to do when you have finished working through the chapter, and so give you extra help in organising your learning. You will probably wish to refer to them when you have finished each chapter.

There are sections of text in this guide which are to be read as in any other book, but much of the guide is concerned with helping you through activities designed to produce effective learning when you work independently. For a fuller explanation of the way APPIL is written you should read the Student's Handbook. What follows is a brief summary.

Q Self-assessment questions

These test your understanding of the work you have done, and will help you to check your progress. They are not intended to be difficult: you should be able to answer most of them quite easily.■

The answers to self-assessment questions are given at the end of the book, but if you look at the answer before you have tried the question you will not be involved in the learning process and your learning may suffer.

Q Development questions

These are included to involve you in a proof or idea which is being developed in the text.■

The answers to these questions are in the text or, for questions marked with an asterisk, at the end of the book. Involving yourself in the development helps you to learn: just looking at the answer is not so effective.

Q Study questions

For these you will need to use resources apart from this guide: for example, textbooks or experimental results. General references are given to basic books at the start of each chapter. You are not expected to consult all the references given, but you should always use more than one when possible.■

This type of question usually requires longer answers than the others. These answers, in many cases, form a basis for your notes for the final examination and are therefore very important. Full answers are not usually given in this guide, though hints and partial answers are sometimes given (these questions are marked with an asterisk). Your answers to study questions should be handed in regularly for marking.

EXTENSIONS

Extensions are provided for several reasons.

(a) To provide additional material of general interest, e.g. applications.

(b) To provide more detailed treatment of some topics.

(c) To provide additional topics, or extensions of core material, to cover the requirements of a particular examination board. In this case, the section is marked SYLLABUS EXTENSION and will be essential study for some students, although others may find it of value. You should consult your teacher if you are not certain whether a particular syllabus extension is appropriate for you.

Use of resources

Audio-visual aids. These are included to supplement your experimental observations.

Background reading. This refers to books which are useful for a more detailed study of certain topics. They are also often interesting to read in their own right, and sometimes put the physics of the syllabus in its historical, social and technological context.

Questions on objectives

These are groups of questions which come at the end of each chapter, and are related to the objectives at the beginning of each chapter. Answering these will help you to tell whether you have achieved the objectives.

Experiments

These are a very important part of the course. The experiments in each chapter are listed at the beginning of the chapter, with an indication of the approximate *laboratory time* required for setting up the apparatus and taking readings. Each experiment is referred to in the text at the most appropriate time. You should aim to organise your work so that it can be done at that time. Full details of experiments are given at the end of the book. Record your results, graphically or in some other way, and your conclusions. There is no value in copying out the instructions given, but notes on special procedures, and any details which might be useful for revision, should be made.

Organising your time

In this programme of work there is a variety of activities. Some of them, like experiments, need a laboratory, and you will also need to use the library. You must, therefore, organise your time so that you can make the best use of the resources available.

When you start a chapter, look through it and see what activities are included, then allocate each activity a time on your work schedule. Make sure, for example, that you do the experiments when you are timetabled in a laboratory. Follow the sequence in this guide if you can, but this may not always be possible.

In the introduction, and at the beginning of each chapter, you will find the recommended time for completion of the work in each chapter. These times are given in units of one week. This assumes that you spend a minimum of 10 hours each week on physics, divided between class time, private study and home study. It is important to try to complete the unit in the stated time. The *progress monitor* will help you plan your time.

End-of-unit test

This is to enable your teacher to check the value of the course to you. You will be asked to do this test when you have completed the unit, and will be given details at the appropriate time.

Introduction to the unit

This is the first of two APPIL units in which you will study waves.

As this unit is one of the recommended starting points for the course, there is a preliminary section, 'Starting block', which reviews some of your earlier physics studies which are relevant to this unit, and includes a preliminary test and advice on how to fill any gaps in your knowledge.

Chapter 1 develops the idea of a wave model by studying the properties of mechanical waves, in springs and on the surface of water.

Chapter 2 introduces a study of sound waves which will be continued in the unit *Vibrations and waves*.

Chapter 3 considers evidence which supports the idea that light is a wave, and shows how some of the properties of light can be explained by assuming this wave model.

Chapter 4 extends your knowledge of the reflection and refraction of light, and shows how these properties are applied to the design of optical instruments.

Recommended study times
You should spend 6 to 7 weeks on this unit, divided roughly as follows:
Chapter 1   2 weeks
Chapter 2   1 week
Chapter 3 $1\frac{1}{2}$ weeks
Chapter 4   2 weeks

In independent learning, students progress through the text at different rates. If you remember your earlier studies of light and sound, you will find that you progress quickly through some parts of chapters 1, 2 and 4.

Contents

Starting block

It is assumed in this unit that you have studied physics before, so the unit will build on and extend your present knowledge. Since you may have forgotten some of the things you learnt, or there may be a few things you are not sure about, this section is designed to help you to revise, re-learn or learn what you need to know to make the best use of this unit.

Start by reading the pre-requisite objectives: these are the things you need to be able to do before you begin work on the main part of the unit.

Then work through the preliminary test, which consists of questions based on the pre-requisite objectives. Work quickly through all parts of the test without reference to books or to any other person. The aim of the test is to enable you to check up on what you know now, so that you can find and fill up any gaps in your own knowledge.

Mark your own test when you have finished, following the marking instructions. Then read the directions for using your test result, and do any follow-up work that is recommended for you.

When you have done this, you will be able to start chapter 1 with the confidence of knowing that you are ready to tackle new work.

Pre-requisite objectives

Before starting this unit you should be able to:

1 Use the following scientific terms correctly: displacement, amplitude, frequency, wavelength, medium, wave, wave speed, period.

2 Interpret a graph of particle displacement plotted against time.

3 Use the following scientific terms correctly: reflection, refraction, real image, virtual image, angle of incidence, angle of reflection, normal, angle of refraction.

4 Recall the relationship between angle of incidence and angle of reflection when light is reflected from a smooth surface.

5 Recall the type and nature of the image formed by a plane mirror.

6 Sketch the paths of rays of light from an object, reflected by a plane mirror to the eye, showing how the image is located.

7 Recall the effect on a ray of light reflected from a plane mirror when the mirror is rotated about an axis perpendicular to the plane containing incident ray, normal and reflected ray.

8 State the meaning of refraction, and sketch the path of rays of light which pass from one medium to another (for example, from air to glass).

9 Recall the effects of a prism on a narrow beam of white light.

10 Use the following scientific terms correctly: converging rays, diverging rays, converging (convex) lens, diverging (concave) lens, focal length, erect image, inverted image, magnification, concave mirror, convex mirror.

11 Explain the difference between a real image and a virtual image.

12 Determine, by graphical construction, the positions, sizes and natures of the images formed by a concave mirror for different positions of the object.

13 Determine, by graphical construction, the positions, sizes and natures of the images formed by a converging lens for different positions of the object.

Preliminary test

There are three types of question in this test, coded as follows:

MC   Multiple choice. Select the single best answer.
MR   Multiple response. Select all the correct answers.
NUM   Numerical answer (including diagrams). Work out the answer and write it down, including the unit where appropriate.

Part A   Wave terms

Questions 1–3 *MC*
Which of the quantities (A–E) below is described in each of the questions 1–3?
A   frequency
B   wavelength
C   period
D   wave speed
E   amplitude

1   The maximum displacement of a particle from its rest position.

2   The number of complete vibrations made in 1 second.

3   The distance between two adjacent crests of a wave.

Questions 4–6 *MC*
Figure P1 shows the waveforms of five notes (A–E), displayed one after the other on a cathode ray oscilloscope, without adjusting its controls.

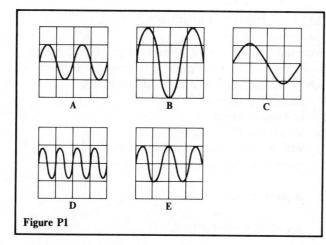

Figure P1

4   Which note has the largest amplitude?

5   Which note has the lowest frequency?

6   Which note has the highest frequency?

Questions 7 and 8 *MR*
The displacement–time graph, figure P2, shows how the displacement of a particle at a particular distance from a source of vibration varies with time. Which of the distances marked (A–G) are equal to the quantities in questions 7 and 8?

7   The period of the vibration.

8   The amplitude of the vibration.

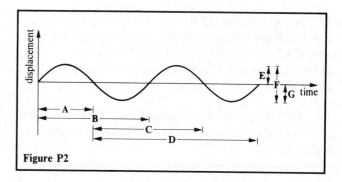

Figure P2

Part B   Reflection and refraction

9   *MC* Which of the following (A–D) shows the image of a letter P placed in front of a plane mirror?
A   P
B   b
C   q
D   d

10   *NUM* A student faces a plane mirror, which is 5 metres in front of her. How far must she move so that she is 4 metres nearer to her image?

11   *NUM* A ray of light strikes a plane mirror so that the reflected ray makes an angle of 30° with the incident ray. The mirror is turned through an angle of 20°, first clockwise then anticlockwise, about an axis at right angles to the plane of the rays. For each case, what is the angle between the incident ray and the new reflected ray?

12 *NUM* An object O is placed between two plane mirrors which are arranged at right angles to each other. The object is 2 cm from one mirror and 3 cm from the other. Sketch a diagram showing the positions of the images that are produced.

13 *MC* Which of the diagrams (A–D) in figure P3 shows correctly the path of a ray of light passing through a glass block?

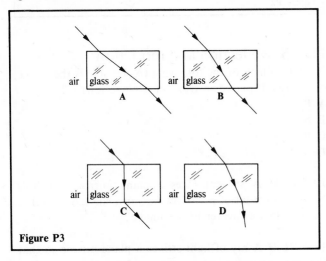

Figure P3

14 *MC* When white light is passed through a prism, which of the following colours is refracted through the smallest angle?

A   yellow
B   red
C   green
D   blue

Part C Mirrors and lenses

Questions 15–19 *MC*

From the descriptions of optical images (A–E) below, choose the correct description for the image formed in each of the cases specified in questions 15–19.

A   real and diminished
B   real and enlarged
C   virtual and diminished
D   virtual and the same size as the object
E   virtual and enlarged

15 A plane mirror.

16 A convex driving mirror.

17 A camera lens used to photograph a distant object.

18 A concave mirror used as a shaving mirror.

19 A converging lens used as a magnifying glass.

20 *MC* An object is placed between a concave mirror and its principal focus. Which of the statements (A–E) correctly describes the image which is formed?

A   virtual, erect and diminished
B   virtual, erect and enlarged
C   real, inverted and diminished
D   real, inverted and the same size as the object
E   real, inverted and enlarged

Questions 21–24 *NUM*

An object 3.0 cm tall is placed 30.0 cm from a concave mirror of focal length 10.0 cm so that it is perpendicular to, and has one end on, the axis of the mirror. Determine, by graphical construction, the answers to questions 21–24.

21 What is the distance of the image from the mirror?

22 What is the height of the image?

23 Is the image erect or inverted?

24 Is the image real or virtual?

Questions 25–27 *MC*

Figure P4 shows a converging lens with five possible *object* positions (A–E) marked on the axis. Select from these the correct object position for each of the types of *image* described in questions 25–27.

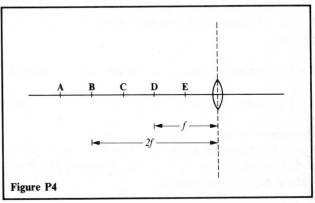

Figure P4

25   Virtual and erect.

26   Real and diminished.

27   Real and enlarged.

Questions 28–32 *NUM*

Figure P5 is a ray diagram (drawn to scale) illustrating the formation of the image of an object 1.0 cm tall, placed 9.0 cm away from the lens.

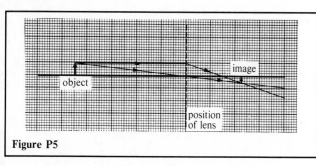

Figure P5

28   What type of lens is used?

29   What is the focal length of the lens?

30   How far is the image from the lens?

31   Is the image real or virtual?

32   What is the magnification of the image?

Questions 33–36 *NUM*

An object 4.0 cm tall is placed 6.0 cm from a converging (convex) lens of focal length 18.0 cm. The object is perpendicular to, and has one end on, the axis of the lens. Determine, by graphical construction, the answers to questions 33–36.

33   What is the distance of the image from the lens?

34   What is the height of the image?

35   Is the image erect or inverted?

36   Is the image real or virtual?

Marking

Compare your answers with those given below, and give yourself one mark for each fully correct answer. To be fully correct, only the one right answer should be given for multiple choice questions, all the right answers and no wrong ones for multiple response questions, and the unit as well as the number for numerical questions. Add up your marks for each part of the test separately.

Answers

Part A   *8 marks*

1 E
2 A
3 B
4 B
5 C
6 D
7 B, C
8 E, G

Part B   *6 marks*

9   C
10 2 metres
11 70°, 10° (figure P6)

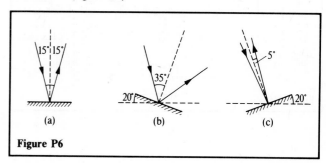

Figure P6

12 Figure P7 shows the positions of all three images.
13 B
14 B

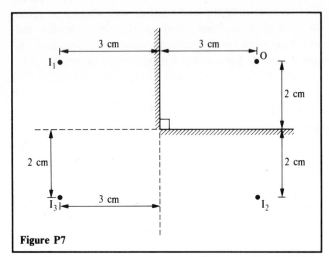

Figure P7

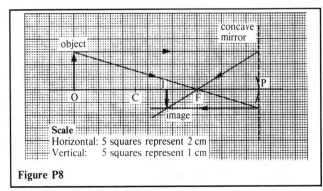

Scale
Horizontal: 5 squares represent 2 cm
Vertical: 5 squares represent 1 cm

Figure P8

Part C   *22 marks*
15 D
16 C
17 A
18 E
19 E
20 B
21 15.0 cm (figure P8)
22 1.5 cm
23 Inverted
24 Real
25 E
26 A
27 C
28 A converging (convex) lens.
29 3.0 cm
30 4.5 cm
31 Real
32 0.5
33 9.0 cm (figure P9)
34 6.0 cm
35 Erect
36 Virtual

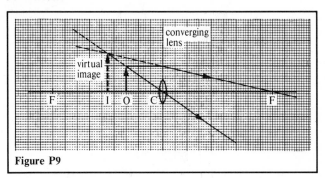

Figure P9

Using the test results
The pre-requisite objectives were tested as follows.

Objectives 1 and 2	Part A
Objectives 3, 4, 5, 6, 7, 8 and 9	Part B
Objectives 10, 11, 12 and 13	Part C

Your marks in the preliminary test indicate whether you need to do some follow-up work before starting chapters 1 and 4. The flow chart will direct you along your own personal route through any necessary revision sections.

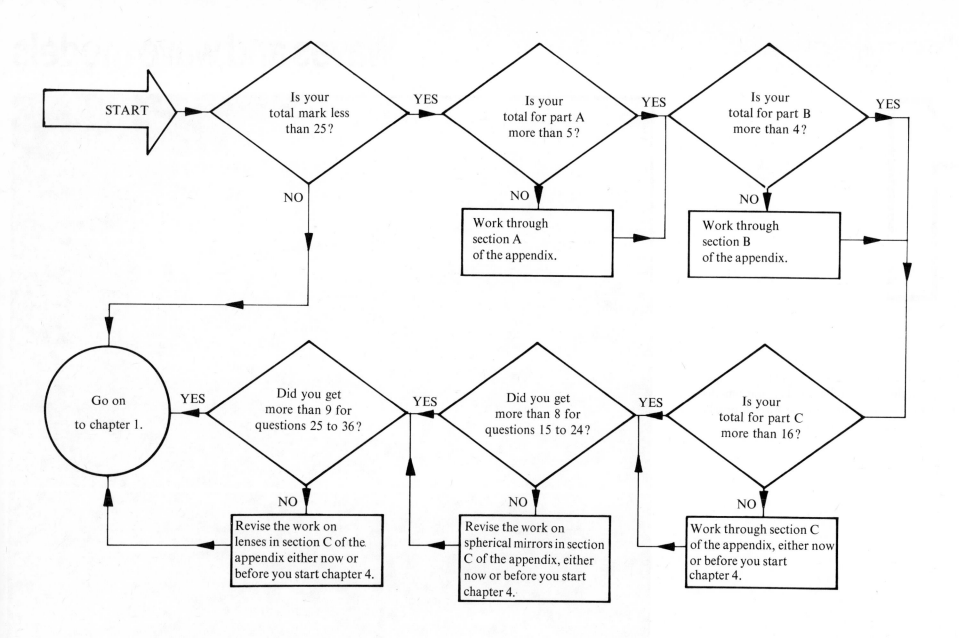

Chapter 1

Waves and wave models

Aim

In this chapter a model of wave motion will be developed by studying the properties of mechanical waves in springs and on the surface of water. This wave model will form the basis for your study of the wave properties of sound and electromagnetic radiations.

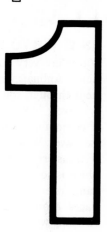

Objectives

When you have completed the work in this chapter you should be able to:

1 Use the following scientific terms correctly: phase angle, phase difference, wave pulse, diffraction, wave train, interference, superposition, mechanical wave, electromagnetic wave, progressive wave, sinusoidal wave.

2 Define the following terms: wavelength, wavefront, amplitude, period, frequency, angular frequency, dispersion.

3 Distinguish between longitudinal and transverse waves, and give examples of each.

4 Derive, recall and use the relationship between wave speed, frequency, and wavelength.

5 Recall examples of reflection of waves, with and without phase change.

6 Predict the forms of the reflected wavefronts when plane or circular waves are reflected from straight or curved barriers.

7 Give qualitative explanations of the refraction and diffraction of waves, with suitable examples.

8 State the principle of superposition.

9 Explain qualitatively, using diagrams, how an interference pattern is produced by superposition of waves from two point sources of the same frequency, and give examples of this phenomenon.

10 Describe, with diagrams and/or graphs, the relationship for a progressive wave between
(a) displacement and time, for a particular point in a medium,
(b) displacement and distance, at a particular instant.

11 SYLLABUS EXTENSION
Outline how an equation of the form $y = a \sin(\omega t - kx)$ can be used to describe a sinusoidal progressive wave, and indicate the physical meaning of the variables and constants in this equation.

Experiments in chapter 1
WP 1   Observing wave pulses
($\frac{3}{4}$ hour)
WP 2   A study of waves in a ripple tank
(1 hour)

References
Akrill	Chapters 16, 17
Bolton	Chapter 6
Duncan FWA	Chapter 6
Nelkon	Chapter 24
Whelan	Chapters 12 and 14

Study time: 2 weeks

1.1 Mechanical waves as a wave model

Waves are very common, varied and important phenomena. Animals, including man, explore their environment through sound and light waves. We communicate by waves; indeed, it is difficult to think of any method of communication, ancient or modern, which does not use waves. Waves also provide the most important means of transferring energy, including the energy of the sun, which is so vital to man's needs on earth. When a wave transfers energy and momentum from the wave source to places around it, we describe it as a *progressive* or *travelling* wave.

In science, models are used to help in explaining observations and predicting effects. A model may be a diagram, a constructed object, a physical situation, or even a mathematical equation. We use models in everyday life. A London underground map is a good model of the underground system. It is certainly not an exact replica of the rail system. For one thing, it is not drawn to scale and the actual lines and trains are not red, brown, yellow or blue as the map suggests. Nevertheless, it is a good model because it can *explain* why if we travel on a certain line we will pass through King's Cross at regular intervals and it can *predict* that if we get on a particular train we can end up in the Essex marshes!

No one can see a *wave* of light, and it is not easy to observe the effects produced when sound travels through air. A wave model helps us to visualise and explain what is happening when waves like light, sound, X-rays, and so on, are produced and transmitted. The wave model will be developed by observing waves in springs, and on the surface of water. These are *mechanical waves*, which are produced when some part of an elastic medium is displaced from its equilibrium position, for example, when a stone is dropped on to a water surface or a loudspeaker makes particles of air vibrate.

Q 1.1 Development question*

Figure 1.1 shows the cross-section of a water surface just after a small stone has been dropped on to it.

(a) How does this diagram support the fact that water is almost incompressible?

(b) What forces act to move particles in the water which are some distance from the stone?

(c) Sketch a section through the water surface a moment after that shown in figure 1.1, marking the reference lines O, X and Y.

(d) What happens to the original kinetic energy of the stone?

(e) Suggest a reason why the water does not immediately become calm again. ■

Note. Answers to development questions are sometimes given at the back of the book, as in this case, but are often incorporated in the question or in the following text.

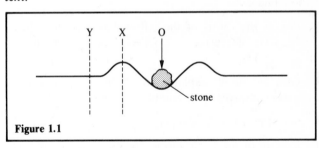

Figure 1.1

Elastic is the term used to describe 'springiness': the capacity of a substance to return to its original shape and size after being deformed. When a particle in an elastic medium is displaced from its equilibrium position, forces act on the particle which will tend to restore it to its original position. Because the particle has inertia (resistance to change in motion), it will overshoot the equilibrium position and oscillate. All the particles in the medium are interconnected by forces, and the displacement of one particle will change the forces acting on other particles close to it. These particles will then be displaced. This interaction between the particles causes a disturbance to spread through the medium and produces a transfer of energy. The moving disturbance is a wave, and the energy transfer can be detected (for example, by a floating cork for water waves or a microphone for sound waves).

A mechanical wave, therefore, transmits mechanical energy through a material medium which has inertia and elasticity.

Electromagnetic waves form a second group of waves. These include light, radio and X-rays. In chapter 3 you will study some evidence that light has wave properties, but a study of the nature of electromagnetic waves and explanation of how they can transmit energy through a vacuum will be deferred until the unit *Vibrations and waves*. However, many of the properties of these complex three-dimensional waves can be understood by studying a simple kind of wave – a one-dimensional wave pulse in a long spring or rope.

1.2 Wave pulses

When you slam the door of a room, the air in the doorway is compressed rapidly. This single compression travels as a disturbance across the room and gives a sudden push to the curtains. The air particles have not travelled across the room in that time, but energy has. This short-duration wave is called a pulse.

Q **1.2 Self-assessment question**
(a) In an obstacle race a competitor has to crawl under a tarpaulin sheet, causing a bump to travel along the sheet. Is this moving disturbance a progressive wave pulse? Explain.
(b) If you look down on a line of cars queuing at traffic lights, you will observe a 'pulse of starting' move along the line of cars when the traffic light changes to green. Which way does the 'pulse of starting' travel, and what does its speed depend on?■

A distinction must always be made between the movement of the particles of the medium and the movement of the wave pulse through the medium.

E **Experiment WP1**
Observing wave pulses
Different types of wave pulse can be observed moving along a stretched spring, and the pulse speeds can be estimated.

Q **1.3 Self-assessment question**
Figure 1.2 shows a series of pictures taken at regular intervals illustrating how a pulse of compressed coils moves along a slinky spring.
(a) Which way does the 10th coil from the left move between instant 2 and instant 4?
(b) Is this coil moving at instant 5? If so, in which direction?
(c) Is it possible to say in which direction this coil is moving at instant 7? Explain.■

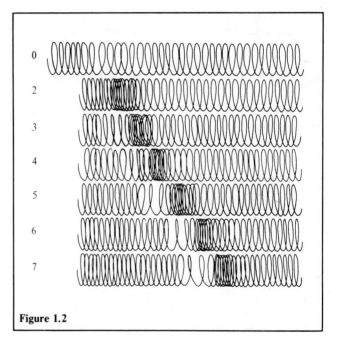

Figure 1.2

The kind of pulse shown in figure 1.2 is a *longitudinal* pulse, which can travel only through a medium which can be compressed. *Transverse* pulses can only travel through a medium in which the particles can be diplaced across the direction in which the pulse travels, and come back.

Twisting the end of a slinky clockwise and then anti-clockwise will produce *torsional* waves, in which particles of the spring have an angular displacement in a plane perpendicular to the direction in which the wave pulse travels. If a violin bow produces torsional waves in a string, a high-pitched squeal is produced. This explains why inexperienced violinists quickly lose their audience!

Q **1.4 Self-assessment question**
What kinds of mechanical waves can be transmitted in
(a) a gas,
(b) a solid?■

Representing waves graphically

In physics we must be able to view the same event in more than one way. Sometimes we view the 'individual trees', sometimes the 'whole wood'. In studying mechanical waves we must consider how a wave travels through a medium (a view of the 'whole wood') and also what happens to individual particles of the medium (a view of each 'tree'). Thus two kinds of graph are used to represent mechanical waves (and other wave motion).
1   Displacement – distance graphs, showing the position (displacement) of every point along the medium at a particular moment of time (displacement y against distance x, for a fixed value of t).
2   Displacement – time graphs, showing what happens to the displacement of a particular point as the time changes (y against t, for a fixed value of x).

Q **1.5 Self-assessment question**
Which type of graph is displayed on a cathode ray oscilloscope showing the waveform of a sound wave picked up by a microphone?■

Q **1.6 Development question**
Figure 1.3a shows the shape of a pulse travelling from left to right along a spring.
(a) Sketch a graph of displacement along the rope at a particular instant (y against x).
(b) Sketch a graph showing how the displacement of P changes as this pulse passes (y against t). Indicate how the y against t graph would change if the wave speed were to be doubled, for this same shape of pulse.
(c) Sketch a graph of y against t for point P if the wave pulse has the same shape but travels with speed c in the opposite direction (figure 1.3b).■

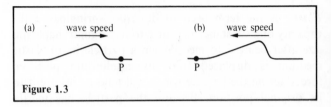

Figure 1.3

Q **1.7 Self-assessment question**
The diagram (figure 1.4) shows a transverse wave pulse in a string travelling at $4\ \mathrm{m\ s^{-1}}$ in the direction of the arrow.
(a) Draw a graph to show precisely how the displacement of P from its equilibrium position varies with time over an interval of 0.3 s from the instant shown in the figure.
(b) How could you find the transverse velocity of P at any instant?■

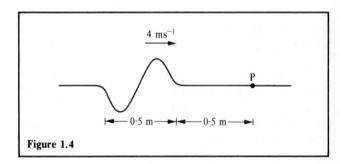

Figure 1.4

Information about the motion of different points in the medium can also be obtained by analysing the position of the pulse at two close successive instants of time. Figure 1.5 shows two such positions of a transverse wave pulse in a rope, in which the particles only move at right angles to the direction of the moving pulse.

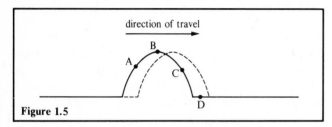

direction of travel

Figure 1.5

Q **1.8 Self-assessment question**
(a) Sketch the diagram (figure 1.5) and mark the displacements of points A, B, C and D during the time interval.
(b) Which points are moving in the same direction?
(c) Which of these points moves with (i) greatest, (ii) least average speed during the interval?
(d) At what point in the pulse is the rope momentarily at rest?■

Superposition of wave pulses

What happens when waves meet? Your observations of wave pulses will have revealed a surprising thing. Waves can pass through each other, and the waves emerge unaffected by this meeting. We can hear music from a radio even though many other sound waves are crossing the line between the radio and our ear. Communication would be impossible if waves bumped into each other as material particles do.

When more than one wave affects the same point in a medium, the waves are said to be *superposed*. The effect is summarised in the *principle of superposition*.

Q **1.9 Study question**
Write a precise statement of the principle of superposition. Illustrate the principle with a graphical example, and indicate why the word 'vector' is important in the statement. Does the principle apply only to wave pulses? What types of wave does it apply to? When does it break down?■

Using references in answering a study question
References are given at the beginning of each chapter. Some are to general physics text books, others are to books on more specific topics. In all the references given you will find parts which are not relevant to a particular question. There are two ways of dealing with this effectively.

1 Use the *index*. Read through the question and choose the *key words* from it, and look for index references to these. In question 1.11, for example, a key word is 'superposition'. Reading more than one explanation will help your understanding.

2 Use *sub-headings* to find relevant sections of the chapters. Skim through these sections and make brief notes of the points you want to include in your answer.

For more help on how to make notes, consult the APPIL *Student's Handbook* and read the relevant chapter in *Use your head* by Tony Buzan.

Q 1.10 Self-assessment question

Figure 1.6 shows two equal and opposite pulses approaching each other on a long string. The pulses are 0.8 m long, each is travelling at 2 m s^{-1}, and their leading edges are 0.4 m apart at the instant shown.

(a) Sketch diagrams to show the shape of the string at times 0.1 s, 0.2 s, 0.3 s, 0.4 s and 0.5 s later than the instant shown.

(b) How does point O move during this period?

(c) Each wave pulse carries energy. What has happened to that energy at $t = 0.3$ s? ■

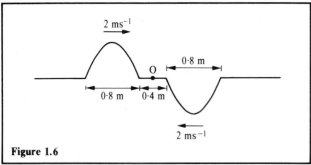

Figure 1.6

Q 1.11 Self-assessment question

Figure 1.7 shows a sequence of photographs taken as two equal symmetrical pulses approach each other along a spring. The spring appears blurred in places, due to its movement during an exposure.

(a) Use the principle of superposition to explain the directions of motion of the blurred sections of spring in photographs 5 and 7.

(b) Explain why there is an instant (photograph 6) when no part of the spring is moving.

(c) How can you tell from the photographs that the sequence of events goes from top to bottom, and not from bottom to top? ■

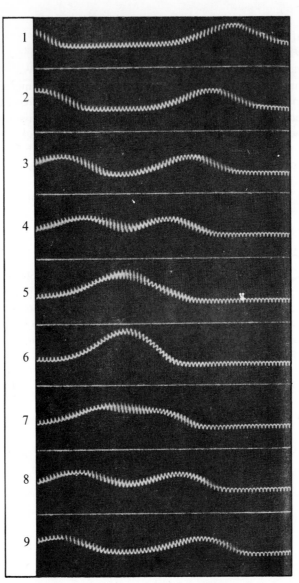

Figure 1.7

Pulses at a boundary

Q 1.12 Self-assessment question

When a transverse pulse on a spring reaches a rigid support, the reflected pulse is upside down. Explain, in terms of the forces on the support and on the spring, why this happens. ■

When a pulse reaches the free end of a spring the only way it can travel is backwards, as a reflected pulse. Since there is no external force acting on the spring, there is no change in the total momentum when the pulse is reflected, so an upright pulse is reflected as an upright pulse.

When a pulse meets a boundary between two media (for example, a light spring and a heavy spring), the energy is partly transmitted through the boundary and partly reflected back. Figure 1.8 shows a pulse travelling from a light spring to a heavy spring. Notice that the reflected pulse is upside down, like that from a rigid support, but some energy is transmitted to the heavy spring.

Q 1.13 Self-assessment question

(a) Compare the speeds of the pulse in the two springs (figure 1.8) and give evidence for your answer.

(b) Suggest what will happen to the way in which the wave energy is divided between transmitted pulse and reflected pulse if the heavy spring is replaced by a still heavier one.

(c) Will any energy be reflected at the junction if the two springs are identical? ■

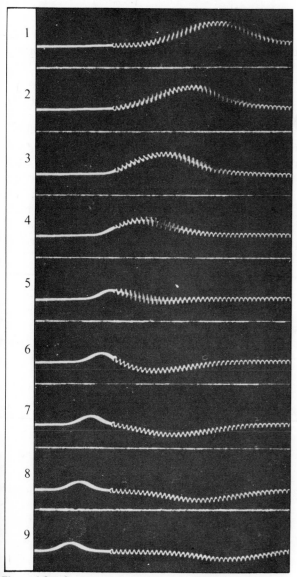

Figure 1.8

What happens when a compression wave pulse is reflected? We cannot now talk of upside-down and right-side-up reflection. However, a compression pulse arriving at a fixed or a free end may produce a reflected compression or a reflected rarefaction.

Q 1.14 Study question
Make notes or draw sketches to show the difference between the reflection of a compression pulse at a fixed and at a free end of a slinky.■

This study of pulses in springs may seem very remote from the study of more important waves like light and sound. However, you will find that this study of pulses provides important clues to understanding topics to be studied later. For example, in the unit *Vibrations and waves* you will study how sound waves can be reflected from both closed and open ends of pipes and how the reflection of light travelling from air to glass is not quite the same as the reflection when light is travelling from glass to air. A single travelling wave pulse which can propagate energy in one dimension only (along the spring) is a good model to study at the beginning.

1.3 Periodic waves

A periodic change is one in which the pattern of change repeats itself at regular intervals: the water level at London Bridge undergoes a periodic change; the motion of a bird's wing in flight is periodic; your pulse is periodic.

The periodic motion of a body can produce a periodic mechanical wave in the surrounding medium. For example, a dipper vibrating in a ripple tank produces a periodic wave train of ripples. A vibrating loudspeaker produces a sound wave: a periodic travelling longitudinal wave.

Q 1.15 Study question
Define the period and the frequency of a periodic change? What is the relationship between period and frequency? In what units is frequency measured?■

There are many kinds of periodic motion. One of the simplest and most common is called simple harmonic motion (s.h.m.). The displacement of an object vibrating with s.h.m. varies with time according to a sinusoidal curve (figure 1.9a). The wavetrain produced by such a source has a sinusoidal profile, so the graph of displacement y against distance x, along a direction of propagation, is as shown in figure 1.9b. Graphs similar to figure 1.9a can be used to describe the variation of the displacement of other points in the vibrating medium with time.

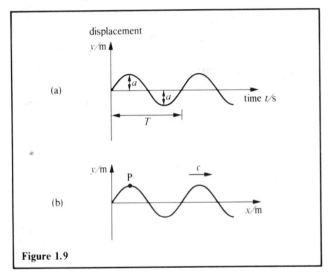

Figure 1.9

Q **1.16 Self-assessment question**
(a) Sketch a graph of y against t for a particle in the vibrating medium which is at P when $t = 0$ (figure 1.9b). Label the amplitude a and the period T on your graph.
(b) How can you find the velocity of the vibrating particle at any instant from the graph?
(c) When is the velocity of the particle (i) maximum, and (ii) zero?
(d) Do particles with the same displacement always have the same velocity? ■

Q **1.17 Development question***
Figure 1.10 shows two instantaneous positions of a periodic wave travelling along a string whose left hand end is attached to a vertically moving vibrator.
(a) Which pairs of points marked on the string have, at the instant shown, (i) the same displacement but velocities in opposite directions, (ii) equal and opposite displacements but the same velocity, (iii) the same displacement and velocity?
(b) In what way is the motion of point B similar to the motion of point A, and in what way is it different?
(c) Which points are vibrating 'in step' (such vibrations are described as *in phase*)?
(d) How far will the waveform travel to the right as the vibrator makes one complete vibration? Explain your answer.
(e) If the distance AE along the wave is 1.2 m, and the vibrator makes a complete vibration in 0.5 s, what is the speed at which the wave crests are travelling? ■

In the last question you considered the motion of five particular points on the string which had displacements of the same size. Now think about the motion of any point on the string.

Q **1.18 Self-assessment question**
(a) What quantities are the same for the vibrations of any two points along the string (assuming no energy is lost as the wave travels along the string)?
(b) Explain the terms *in phase* and *phase lag* by referring to vibrating points on the string in figure 1.10.
(c) 'The distance between two consecutive points which are in phase is constant, for a wave of fixed speed and frequency.' Explain and justify this statement, referring to figure 1.10. ■

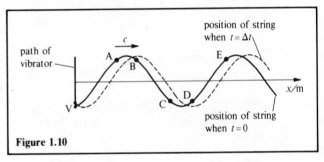

Figure 1.10

Q 1.19 Self-assessment question
(a) Show that
wave speed = frequency × wavelength,
➤ $c = f\lambda$.
(b) What changes would you observe in a ripple tank if you reduced the frequency of the vibrating dipper?
(c) The speed of radio waves is 3×10^8 m s^{-1}. What is the frequency of the waves broadcasting Radio 4 on 1500 m? ■

Q 1.20 Self-assessment question
Figure 1.11 is a graph of y against x for a wave travelling with speed c. Draw the corresponding y against t graph for point P, marking the value of t for each instant when $y = 0$. Express these values of t in terms of λ and c. ■

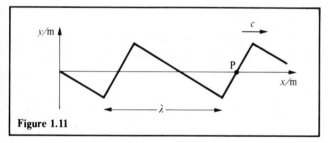

Figure 1.11

1.4 Equations for a sinusoidal wave

Equation for a vibrator

Q 1.21 Study question
The motion of a vibrator moving with s.h.m. can be represented by the equation $y = a \sin \omega t$, where a and ω are constants for the vibration.
(a) Sketch a graph showing how displacement varies with time for such a vibrator. Mark the maximum value of the displacement and the values of the time t (in terms of π and ω) at which y is maximum, minimum or zero.
(b) What do the symbols a and ω represent? How is ω related to the period T and the frequency f?
(c) Write two alternative forms of the equation
$$y = a \sin \omega t,$$
giving y in terms of a, T and t, or in terms of a, f and t. ■

Q 1.22 Self-assessment question
Plot a graph of $y = a \sin \omega t$, if $a = 10$ mm and $\omega = \pi/6$ rad s^{-1}. Plot whole number values of t from $t = 0$ to $t = 12$ s. State the amplitude and period of the vibration. What is the value of the displacement when $t = 7$ s? ■

Equations for some points in the medium

Figure 1.12 shows a wave in a long string under tension which is connected to a vibrator. The vibrator is moving with simple harmonic motion, and the diagram shows the position of the string and vibrator when $t = 0$. The vibrator has zero displacement when $t = 0$, with the displacement becoming positive as t increases from zero. Figure 1.13a shows the motion of vibrator V and its motion must be described by the equation $y = a \sin \omega t$. As the wave travels down the string the points P, Q, R and S all vibrate with s.h.m. of the same amplitude and frequency as the vibrator, but the equation $y = a \sin \omega t$ does not describe the motion of any of these points.

Points P, Q, R and S are at different stages of their vibrations when $t = 0$, that is, their vibrations have different *phases*. Figure 1.13b represents the motion of a point which moves upwards through the centre when $t = \pi/2\omega$, and reaches its maximum upward displacement $\pi/2\omega$ after V. This motion lags behind the motion shown in figure 1.13a by $\pi/2\omega$, and the equation for the motion described in figure 1.13b is $y = a \sin(\omega t - \pi/2)$, where $\pi/2$ is the phase lag, expressed in radians.

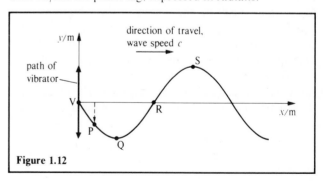

Figure 1.12

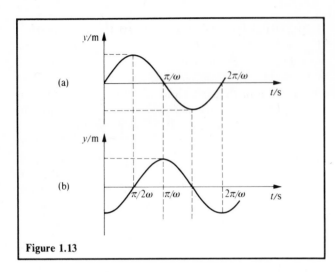

(a)

(b)

Figure 1.13

Q **1.23 Self-assessment question**

(a) Show that the equation $y = a \sin(\omega t - \pi/2)$ agrees with figure 1.13b for $t = 0, \pi/2\omega$ and π/ω.

(b) State, with reasons, which point on the string in figure 1.12 has the motion described by figure 1.13b.

(c) Sketch graphs to represent the motion of points R and S on the string.

(d) By how much do the phases of the vibrations of R and S lag behind the vibration of V? Write equations describing the motions of points R and S, and check that the equations agree with the graphs you have drawn when $t = 0$ or $\pi/2\omega$.

(e) What can you say about the value of the phase lag if the vibrating point is further from the vibrator than S? ■

SYLLABUS EXTENSION

Equation of a travelling wave

Consider the motion of a point such as P (figure 1.12) in a travelling wave. The vibration of Q lags behind the vibration of P because the wave is travelling to the right. You deduced in question 1.23 that the lag of R is twice as big as the lag of Q, so doubling the distance from V doubles the phase lag. Also, the lag of S is three times the lag of Q. The phase lag ϕ at any point is thus proportional to the distance x from the vibrating source. The phase lag ϕ at P $= kx$, where k is a constant.

Q **1.24 Development question***

(a) Write an equation describing how the displacement y of point P, with phase lag ϕ, varies with time t.

(b) Write an equation describing how the displacement y of point P, distance x from the vibrator, varies with time t.

(c) What is the value of the phase lag kx when $x = \lambda$? Express k in terms of λ.

(d) Rewrite the equation from part (b), expressing k in terms of λ and ω in terms of T.

(e) Rewrite the equation obtained in (d) in terms of the frequency f and the wave speed c. ■

The three equations you have obtained describe how the displacement of *any* point in the medium varies with both time and distance from the source as the wave travels along. Since the various forms of the equation are equivalent, you do not need to remember all of them: one is sufficient. From that one, in solving problems, you can obtain the form of the equation which matches the data provided.

Q **1.25 Self-assessment question**

A wave travelling along a horizontal string is represented by the equation

$$y = a \sin(\omega t - kx),$$

where y is the vertical upward displacement at a point, distance x from the source, and $a = 0.05$ m, $\omega = 10\pi$ rad s^{-1} and $k = 2.5\pi$ rad m^{-1}.

(a) What is the frequency of the wave motion?

(b) What is the wavelength?

(c) At what speed does the wave travel?

(d) Sketch the shape of the string when (i) $t = 0$, (ii) $t = 1/20$ s.

(e) Write down an equation which describes the motion of a point on this string at a distance of 2 m from the origin.

(f) The source of the wave is a moving vibrator. What was the displacement of the vibrator from its equilibrium position at $t = 0$? In which direction was it moving at that instant?

(g) What equation would describe a wave of the same amplitude and wavelength travelling in the opposite direction? ■

EXTENSION

Superposition of sinusoidal waves

What happens when two or more sine waves are superposed? Using the principle of superposition, we can find the resulting disturbance by adding up the constituent waves, if the displacements are in the same plane. Consider first what happens when two sine waves of the same frequency are superposed.

Q **1.26 Self-assessment question**
The graphs (figure 1.14) represent the time variations of the displacements produced at a point P in a medium by two sine waves of the same frequency but different phase and amplitude. Sketch a graph to show how the displacement at P varies with time when these two waves superpose.■

The result is interesting, and perhaps unexpected: when two sine waves of the same frequency are superposed the resultant is always a sine wave, even though the two constituent waves differ in phase and amplitude. Part of a sound wave produced by a flute (almost a perfect sine wave) may travel directly to our ear while another part of the wave reaches us after reflection and has a smaller amplitude than the direct wave and is out of phase with it. These waves are superposed at our ear to produce a resulting sine wave and so we still recognise the sound as coming from a flute. Here is some evidence which explains our common experience that sounds are not distorted beyond recognition when they reach us by different paths from the original source.

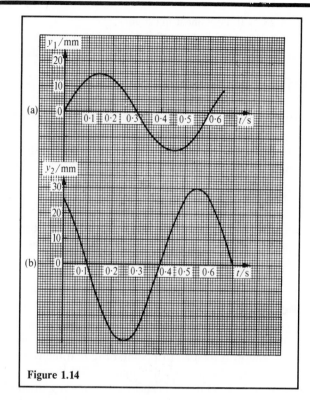

Figure 1.14

Now consider what happens when sinusoidal waves of different frequencies are superposed.

Q **1.27 Self-assessment question**
Sketch the two wave forms whose frequencies are in the ratio 1:2 (figure 1.15), and draw the resultant wave form produced by superposition.■

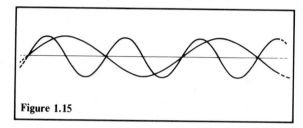

Figure 1.15

The resultant wave has a complex shape, but the shape repeats itself at regular intervals. The wave is therefore a periodic wave. This is true however many waves of differing frequencies are superposed. The converse of this statement is even more important. Known as *Fourier's theorem*, it states:

Any periodic wave motion, however complex, can be shown to be the sum of a series of simple harmonic (sinusoidal) waves of appropriate frequency and amplitude.

Electronic synthesizers produce a wide variety of sounds by summing up a series of sine wave vibrations. Even more remarkably, our ears can analyse complex sounds into their constituent harmonic frequencies.

1.5 Wave behaviour in two dimensions

So far in this chapter the properties of waves have been studied using a one-dimensional wave model – a wave on a string. Now we can extend our study by observing what happens in a plane in two-dimensional space. We can do this by looking at two-dimensional waves (e.g. ripples on a water surface) and also by considering the effects produced in a particular plane by three-dimensional waves.

Wavefronts

A wavefront is a surface containing all points for which the disturbance has the same phase. We can also think of a wavefront as the surface containing all points in the moving wave which left the source at the same instant. For one-dimensional waves the wavefront is a moving point and for two-dimensional waves the wavefront is a line. A circular crest radiating from a point disturbance of a water surface is a wavefront; so also is a radiating trough, or any other line on the surface which satisfies the definition above. When representing periodic waves we often draw a series of wavefronts which differ in phase by 2π rad (that is, at separations of one wavelength).

Wavefronts move outwards from the source, and lines drawn perpendicular to the wavefront indicate the direction in which energy is radiating. In the study of light we refer to these lines as *rays*, but the term can be applied to all kinds of radiating energy waves.

Q 1.28 Self-assessment question
(a) What kind of wavefront is produced by a point source if the wave speed is the same for all directions in the medium?
(b) How would you draw this wavefront in a plane passing through the point source?
(c) If plane wavefronts arrive at a long narrow slit, what shape are the emerging wavefronts?
(d) How would you draw these wavefronts in a plane perpendicular to the length of the slit?■

E Experiment WP 2
A study of waves in a ripple tank
Wave pulses and continuous waves on a water surface are used to obtain evidence about the general properties of waves.

Reflection of waves

Observations in the ripple tank show how water waves obey the laws of reflection. They can be reflected so that the wave energy is focused to a point, or so that the waves appear to come from a 'virtual image point'. You may have already studied these effects by observing ray streaks (streaks of light perpendicular to the wavefront); in the ripple tank you observe the wavefronts themselves. So there are two different ways of describing and visualising the same effects.

Q 1.29 Self-assessment question
In figure 1.16 a straight wave pulse approaches a right-angled reflector at an angle of $45°$.
(a) In what direction does the pulse travel after reflection at both surfaces?
(b) What happens if the pulse is incident at some other angle?■

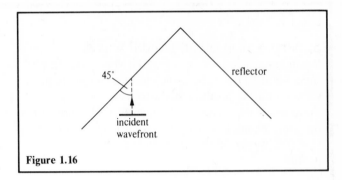

Figure 1.16

Q 1.30 Self-assessment question
(a) Figure 1.17 shows two sets of ripples which had a common point source. State the direction of travel of each wave pulse, and explain how this pattern has been formed.
(b) Give reasons why the plane wave shows a stronger contrast between dark and bright areas than the circular wave.
(c) Estimate the proportion of the total wave energy carried by the circular wave.■

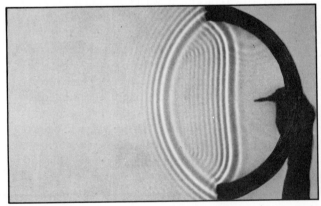

Figure 1.17

Refraction of waves

From qualitative observations in a ripple tank, the following points can be deduced.

1 Ripples travel more slowly in shallow water than in deep water.

2 The change in velocity produces a change in wavelength, but no change in frequency.

3 The change in velocity produces a change in the direction of the wavefront (except when the incident wavefront is parallel to the boundary). If the wave travels across a boundary into a medium in which the wave velocity is reduced, then the wavefronts became more nearly parallel to the boundary.

Q 1.31 Self-assessment question
A ripple tank is not levelled correctly and, when the water surface is disturbed at a point, a wavefront like that shown in figure 1.18 is produced. Describe how the tank is sloping and give reasons for your answer. ■

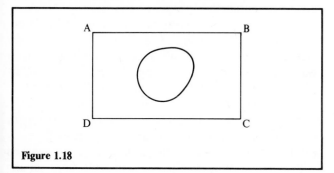

Figure 1.18

Q 1.32 Self-assessment question
Figure 1.19 shows a straight wavefront approaching a coastline. Assume that the sea has constant depth up to the line AB, but beyond AB the sea gets steadily shallower at a rate determined by the coastline shape.
(a) Sketch possible wavefronts as the waves travel to the beach.
(b) Draw in normals to these wavefronts to show the direction of energy flow, and explain why the sea is always calmer in a bay than on a headland. ■

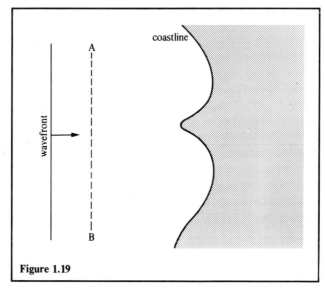

Figure 1.19

Q 1.33 Self-assessment question
Figures 1.20a and 1.20b show the refraction of ripples of different frequencies at the boundary of a shallow region. The angle of incidence is the same in each case, and so is the position of the black marker. Which frequency has been refracted most? ■

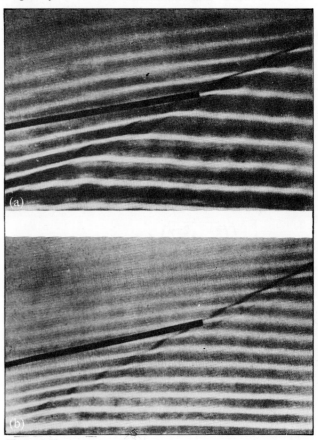

Figure 1.20

The refraction of ripples of different frequency through different angles is an example of *dispersion*. This effect is produced when the speed of a wave in a medium depends on the wave frequency (and so also on its wavelength). The medium is then described as a *dispersive medium*. A single complex shaped pulse in a rope may change its shape as it travels, because a rope is a dispersive medium. The complex pulse is made up of several sine wave pulses of different frequency, and these different frequencies travel at different speeds in the dispersive medium and cause the pulse shape to change. Fortunately air is not a dispersive medium for sound waves, otherwise the shape of the sound wave would change as it travelled and sounds would 'sound' different at different distances from the source.

Q 1.34 Study question
The speed v of waves on the surface of deep water is given by

$$v = \sqrt{\left(\frac{g\lambda}{2\pi} + \frac{2\pi\gamma}{\lambda\rho}\right)}$$

where γ is the surface tension and ρ is the density of the water.
(a) Explain how this equation shows that water is a dispersive medium.
(b) Show from the formula that the speed of surface *ripples* produced by a high frequency vibrator is mainly determined by surface tension effects, whereas the speed of long wavelength waves on the ocean is mainly determined by gravity.
(c) 'The feature which distinguishes gravity waves from ripples is the type of restoring mechanism'. Explain this statement. ■

Q 1.35 Self-assessment question
Ocean waves have such long wavelengths that surface tension effects are negligible. Waves of various frequencies are generated by storms at sea. Use the equation given in question 1.34 to calculate the speeds of ocean waves of wavelengths 10 m and 20 m. If the storm occurs 2000 km from land, how much sooner will the faster group arrive than the slower? Comment on your answer and say how it explains a newspaper headline such as 'Atlantic rollers hit the West Coast of Britain'. ■

Interference

If circular ripples are generated by two dippers attached to the same vibrating bar, the superposed ripples form a steady pattern which we call an interference pattern. The vibrating dippers are described as *coherent* sources.

Sources are coherent if they have the same frequency, and a constant phase relationship (always in phase or always out of phase by the same amount). If a pattern is to be observed, the two waves should have similar amplitudes. If the waves are transverse, the two coherent sources must produce displacements in the same plane (that is, the waves must be polarised in the same plane or unpolarised – this statement will be explained in the unit *Vibrations and waves*).

Q 1.36 Development question*
Figure 1.21 shows circular waves radiating from two coherent sources of ripples vibrating in phase. The arcs show the positions of wavecrests at a particular instant.
(a) Where is the water level at each point marked with a dark circle at the instant recorded?
(b) Where will the water level be at each dark circle half a period later?
(c) What happens to the water level at each dark circle during one whole period? Does the water surface move in exactly the same way at each dark circle?
(d) Consider points marked with a blank circle, such as Q. How does the movement of the water surface at Q resemble that at points marked with dark circles, and how does it differ?
(e) What can you say about the amplitude of vibration at one point along a line, like A_1, of dark and blank circles? Are there any points on the surface which have greater amplitude?
(f) A point in a wave where the vibration has maximum amplitude is called an antinode. A_0 and A_1 are *antinodal lines*. What is the path difference at point P between waves travelling to P from S_1 and S_2? Is the path difference the same for all other points along line A_1?
(g) Find the path difference for points along A_3 and A_4 and hence deduce a general expression for the path difference for any point on an antinodal line.
(h) Describe the state of the surface at points marked with a cross. Why can you describe the lines joining these points as nodal lines?
(i) Find the path difference at point R on line N_3 and hence deduce what the path differences must be along the nodal lines N_3 and N_4. ■

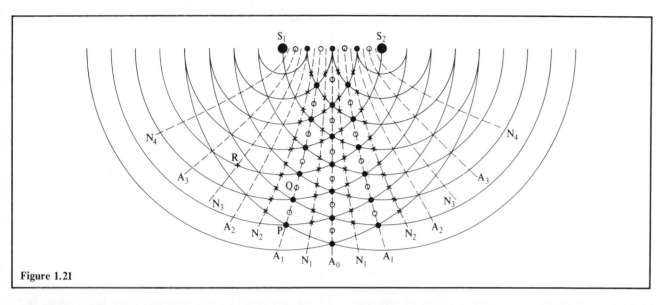

Figure 1.21

Q **1.37 Self-assessment question**

Figure 1.22 shows interference patterns from two sources. The sources are the same distance apart in figures 1.22a and 1.22b. The frequency of the vibration is the same in figures 1.22a and 1.22c. Use the photographs to suggest how the separation x of adjacent nodal points, at a distance D from the source, depends on (i) the distance D, (ii) the source separation d, and (iii) the wavelength of the ripples λ. Hence suggest a possible relationship between x and these quantities.■

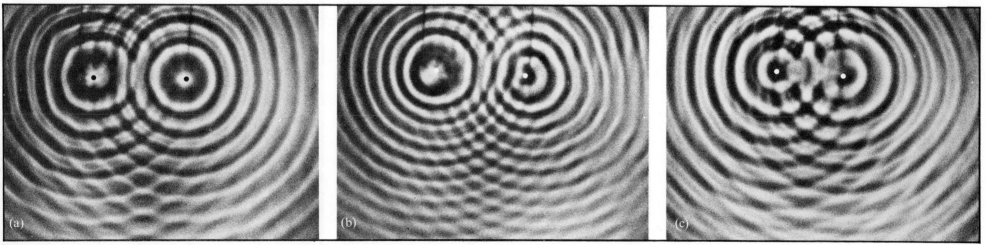

Figure 1.22

Q **1.38 Self-assessment question**

Two dippers placed 9 cm apart are vibrating in phase at a frequency of 8 Hz. They produce ripples travelling at a speed of 24 cm s^{-1}. There are points along the line joining the dippers where the water is calm (nodes).

(a) How far from the mid-point of the line joining the sources is the nearest nodal point?

(b) How many nodes will there be along the line joining the sources?

(c) The dippers are now attached to separate vibrating bars so that they vibrate at the same frequency, 8 Hz, but are now out of phase by π rad (half a period). How does this affect the position and separation of the nodes?

(d) What will happen if the frequency of one dipper changes to 8.1 Hz?■

Diffraction

Ripple tank experiments show that when a plane wave passes through an aperture the shape of the wavefront changes and the wave energy spreads round the corner of the obstacle. This effect is called *diffraction*, and it occurs whenever a wave passes an obstacle or passes through an aperture (diffraction effects are analysed in detail in the unit *Vibrations and waves*).

Q **1.39 Study question**

(a) Describe how the shape of the diffracted wavefront and the distribution of the wave energy changes as the size of the aperture is steadily decreased. Are there any lines of calm water in the pattern?

(b) If waves of a range of frequencies pass through the same aperture, for which frequencies are the diffraction effects relatively more important?

(c) Sketch the diffracted wavefronts from an aperture whose width is one wavelength.■

AV **WP 1 Filmloop**
Ripple tank diffraction

AV **WP 2 Filmloop**
Ripple tank interference

These filmloops provide an opportunity to review and consolidate your experimental work.

Comprehension exercise

THE BIG WAVE

The tsunami or tidal wave is one of the most destructive natural phenomena known to man. It has produced some of the worst disasters in recorded history. Perhaps the most famous tsunami in recent times was that formed by the explosion of the volcanic island of Krakatoa in 1883. It raced across the western Pacific ocean at nearly 500 km/h, raising waves 30 to 40 metres high on the coasts of Java and Sumatra that killed over 27 000 people and swept everything away before them. One or two such disasters occur in the Pacific each century, while several tsunamis every decade cause loss of life, great property damage and extensive flooding.

The popular name 'tidal wave' is a misnomer. The wave is not produced by any solar or lunar tide effects, but is generated as a result of underwater earthquakes, volcanic eruptions or landslides. Nor is the idea of a single giant wave correct. A tsunami is a series of waves with the largest crest in the middle. Moreover these giant waves are produced only as the sea disturbance approaches the land.

Everything about these waves is extraordinary. Their wavelengths in deep ocean may be 150 km to 250 km (compared with 300 m for the longest wind-produced sea wave). Wind waves rarely travel at more than 90 km/h but the velocity of tsunamis varies as the square of the water depth, and in the deepest waters of the Pacific they reach a staggering 800 km/h. One final unique feature of these waves is that in the deepest parts of the ocean their amplitude may be only three metres or so.

As a tsunami approaches land the forward region of the wave pulse is slowed down as the depth decreases. The wavelength is dramatically reduced, causing a build-up of the crests. In this way a 5 m high crest travelling at 600 km/h becomes a 30 m high wave travelling at 50 km/h. When such a wave struck Hilo Bay in Hawaii in 1946, the crews of ships moored 2 km offshore watched horrified as a wave which had passed them as a wave of amplitude 1.5 m then built up into a 10 m wall of water as it reached the shore. This particular wave, generated by an earthquake in the Aleutian Islands, had travelled 3400 km in only five hours.

The first effect of the arrival of a tsunami on a coast is a minor wave, which raises the sea level by a metre or two (figure 1.23). This is followed about 15 minutes later by a trough, which appears to take the sea out to low tide (hence the term tidal wave). The heights of incoming crests and troughs increase, until the sea retreats well below low tide level just before the arrival of the main giant wave.

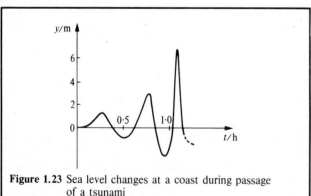

Figure 1.23 Sea level changes at a coast during passage of a tsunami

Although man will never prevent the occurrence of destructive tsunamis, warning systems have now been set up which enable endangered populations to be evacuated from threatened coastlines. When a large earthquake occurs, tsunami-watchers calculate its epicentre. If it is likely to produce a tsunami wave, stations all over the Pacific are alerted to detect shock waves and predict the possible arrival times of the tsunami at hundreds of populated areas. In this way warning was given of the 1960 tsunami generated by an earthquake in Chile, and though it caused extensive damage the death toll was dramatically reduced because of the warning system.

Questions

1   Explain how the amplitude of a tsunami increases, and indicate why this does not contradict the principle of energy conservation.

2   A tsunami had a speed of 47 km/h where the ocean depth was 1300 m. Its maximum speed reached 750 km/h. What can you deduce from this?

3   Using any relevant data, estimate a typical wavelength in the forward part of a tsunami as it approaches land.

Comprehension exercise

ENERGY FROM WAVES

As it becomes clear that the energy provided by oil and natural gas will be greatly depleted by the end of the century, decisions must be made about how much of future energy needs will be provided by widespread adoption of nuclear power, expansion of the coal industry or the development of alternative 'renewable' energy sources (e.g. solar, tidal, wind and wave energy).

With a long coastline and some extremely rough seas, Britain is in a good position to turn wave power into useful energy. The government has already committed over £10 million to research into alternative energy sources, and one quarter of this has been used to support research into wave power systems.

Since the most useful renewable energy sources provide an intermittent supply, it is not intended that these sources should replace conventional power stations as providers of the *base load* but that they should be used as *fuel savers*.

Wave power is appealing, not just because there is plenty of it – a dozen wave power stations, each 50 miles long, would supply half of Britain's energy needs – but also because it is available in greatest quantity when energy demands are high, during winter, when solar energy is at its lowest availability.

Wave energy should not be confused with tidal energy. Tidal energy is available because of the difference in sea level at different times of the day. It can be extracted by building estuary barrages, as at La Rance in France and as proposed for the Severn estuary. Wave energy is available because of the movement of huge masses of water as the water level rises and falls during the passage of a wave.

Four different wave energy systems are being studied and developed in Britain today: (a) Salter ducks, (b) Cockerell contour rafts, (c) Russell rectifiers and (d) the oscillating water column. The first three are British ideas, the last concept comes from Japan.

In all four systems the basic problems to be solved are
(i) *how to convert* the motion of a raft or vane, or of the water itself, into a form of energy which can be transmitted to the land;
(ii) *how to transmit* the energy to the mainland;
(iii) *how to moor* the system effectively many miles from land;
(iv) *how to increase* the efficiency of the energy extraction.

The Salter system is a series of vanes arranged in a long string (figure 1.24). The 'ducks' oscillate to and fro as the wave passes, and are shaped so that they extract maximum energy from the waves. The rocking motion of the ducks must provide energy to drive a generator or alternatively to work a pump which will drive a generator. One of the key problems to be solved is the design of the spine. The line of ducks has to be arranged sideways on to the wave, and this is a position which ships avoid at all costs because it creates a lot of strain in the structure when one end is lifted higher than the other. The research programme illustrates the value of developing a system using a series of scale models. 1/150 scale

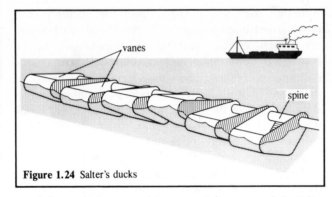

Figure 1.24 Salter's ducks

models are being tested in a special wave tank in Edinburgh; preparations are underway for testing a 1/10 scale duck string 50 metres long on Loch Ness.

The Russell rectifier (figure 1.25) is a wave rectifier (i.e. a box which only allows a one-way flow of water). The rectifier consists of a large box divided into a high level reservoir and a lower level reservoir with valves (vertical non-return flaps) in the sides. These valves allow water from a crest to flow into the high level reservoir and also allow the low level reservoir to empty into the sea when a trough passes by. The different water levels in the rectifier provide hydraulic pressure capable of driving a specially designed turbine-generator which can operate on low pressures.

The oscillating water column idea was developed when Masuda, a Japanese inventor, was investigating floating breakwaters. He found that wave energy could be extracted if the breakwater was made in the form of an inverted box held with its open end under water like an 'inverted can' (figure 1.26). The incoming waves set up oscillations in the water column trapped inside the 'up-

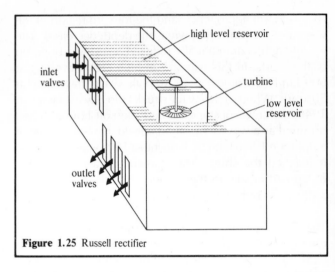

Figure 1.25 Russell rectifier

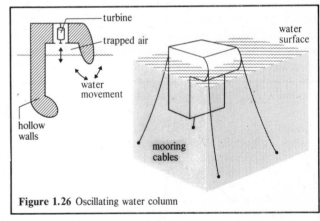

Figure 1.26 Oscillating water column

turned can', and the wave was made to do work by forcing air in and out of holes at the top of the can. Air turbines or fluid turbines could then be used to extract energy from the system.

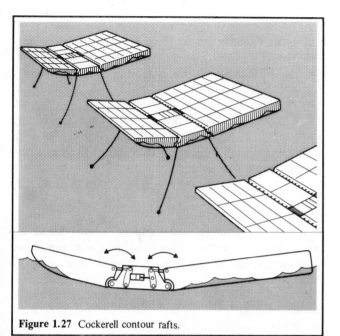

Figure 1.27 Cockerell contour rafts.

Contour rafts are the brainchild of Christopher Cockerell, the inventor of the hovercraft. This device (figure 1.27) consists of a chain of rafts, hinged so that the rafts can follow the contour of the wave as the wave moves down the chain. This means that adjacent rafts in the chain will rotate relative to each other. Hydraulic motors or pumps between each raft can then convert this rotation into pressure pulses to drive a generator.

Models of the full-scale rafts are now being tested in the Solent. Waves here are approximately 1/10th the height of those to be found at the full-size sites and so provide an ideal scaled down experiment for testing performance and mooring problems.

What is the best size for a raft? Obviously a large ship moves less in the waves than a small raft. The size of each hinged float must relate to the smallest waves it will experience rather than the biggest. Sections longer than about a quarter of a wavelength would quickly lose efficiency as length increased. To suit typical Atlantic conditions west of the Hebrides, a raft has been designed which is 107 m long with hinged sections about 30 m long. The proposed full-scale raft will be 50 m wide. The model rafts being tried out in the Solent are expected to generate only a kilowatt, but it is calculated that a full-size raft of the dimensions stated above will generate 2 megawatts peak or 1 megawatt average. A 500 megawatt power station might consist of a series of rafts 5 to 10 miles offshore, stretching over a length of 15 miles parallel to the coast.

The rate of generation of electric power by a wave power station will be subject to great fluctuations depending on the sea conditions and time of year. Some means may have to be found of smoothing out the variations by storing the product. One method of doing this is to use the electricity generated by the waves to pump water to a high level reservoir which provides a store of energy for subsequent electricity generation. Another possibility is to store the energy as a manufactured chemical: the wave power electricity would be used to smelt aluminium or manufacture hydrogen. The hydrogen can then be stored in disused natural gas fields and utilized subsequently in the manufacture of fertilizers. Large areas of the world are short of both energy and fertilizer—a wave powered fertilizer plant may be one answer to the problem.

One thing seems certain. We have now reached the stage where wave power systems are moving rapidly from the laboratory development stage into the real world of heavy engineering design. We are moving a step nearer to realising the ambition of turning the immense power of the waves to man's benefit.

Questions

1   What is meant by the term *renewable* when applied to energy sources?

2   What is the difference between tidal power and wave power?

3   What advantages are there in testing a model of Salter's ducks in a special wave generating tank? Why is the Solent a good place for testing model contour rafts?

4   What special characteristic must the turbine in a Russell rectifier have?

5   State two ways in which the Masuda column (figure 1.26) differs in design from a simple 'inverted can' and suggest reasons for this design.

6   Why are the Cockerell rafts called *contour* rafts? What factors must be taken into account in deciding on the best size for each hinged section and for the whole raft system?

7   How can wave power systems providing a very variable power output be utilized effectively?

Questions on objectives

Before you attempt these, check through the list of objectives for this chapter and make sure that your notes on the chapter have not left out anything important.

1 When a sinusoidal progressive mechanical wave of constant amplitude passes through a medium, which of the following statements are *true* and which are *false*?
(a) All particles vibrate with s.h.m. with the same frequency as the source.
(b) Particles vibrate with the same frequency but with different amplitudes.
(c) All particles have the same amplitude of vibration.
(d) Particles vibrate in phase with the source.
(e) Particles in the same wavelength have the same phase.
(f) The distance between adjacent particles in phase is constant.
(g) All particles within one wavelength have different phases.

(objectives 1 and 2)

2 Use the definitions of wavelength, frequency, and wave speed to obtain an equation relating these quantities. Sound can be recorded on tape which is magnetized as it passes a narrow gap between the poles of an electromagnet. The sound wave pattern is reproduced by the magnetizing current in the coil. When the recorder is run with a tape speed of 17 cm s⁻¹, it is capable of recording and reproducing frequencies up to 10 kHz.
(a) What length of tape records one cycle of 10 kHz sound?

(b) Suggest a maximum size for the gap if the recorder is to reproduce 10 kHz sound accurately.
(c) What will the upper frequency limit be when the machine is run at 4.25 cm s⁻¹?

(objectives 2, 4)

3 Figure 1.28 shows six sketches of pulses in a heavy spring (left) joined to a lighter spring. Three of the sketches represent different instants in one event and the other three represent instants in a different event.
(a) Arrange the figures in two groups, in the correct sequences. Sketch the groups, indicating the direction of the wave pulse in each case.
(b) Explain how the sketches provide evidence that (i) wave energy is shared between transmitted and reflected pulses, (ii) the speed of the wave is greater in one spring than in the other, and (iii) the relative phase of reflection is determined by the direction of movement of the pulse when springs of different mass are joined.

(objective 5)

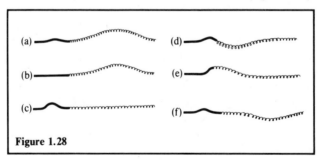

Figure 1.28

4 A circular wave pulse travels at a speed of 20 cm s⁻¹ to a plane reflector placed 10 cm from the source. Draw the wavefronts 0.7 s after the pulse left the source, indicating the scale of your diagram.

(objective 6)

5 Which of the following are altered when a travelling wave crosses a boundary between two media with different physical properties: velocity, frequency, wavelength, amplitude, phase?

(objectives 1, 7)

6 Earthquake waves are of two kinds, primary waves which are longitudinal and secondary waves which are transverse. Only one of these kinds of waves can travel through the earth's core. Suggest which one, and say what you can deduce about the earth's core.

(objective 3)

7 What is a dispersive medium?

(objective 7)

8 Figure 1.29 shows a graph of y against x for a travelling wave at a particular instant. Sketch the corresponding graph of y against t for point P, one second after the instant shown.

(objective 10)

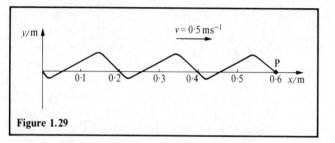

Figure 1.29

9 State the principle of superposition.

The map (figure 1.30) shows part of a coastline, with two land-based radio navigation stations A and B. Both stations transmit continuous sinusoidal radio waves with the same amplitude and same wavelength (200 m). A ship X, exactly midway between A and B, detects a signal whose amplitude is twice that of either station alone.

(a) What can be said about the signals from the two stations?

(b) The ship X travels to a new position by sailing 100 m in the direction shown by the arrow. What signal will it now detect? Explain this.

(c) A ship Y also starts at a position equidistant from A and B and then travels in the direction shown by the arrow. Exactly the same changes to the signal received were observed as in the case of ship X in (b). Explain whether Y has sailed 100 m, more than 100 m, or less than 100 m.

(objectives 8 and 9)

10 EXTENSION

When a sinusoidal progressive wave passes through a medium, the displacement y in metres of a particle A varies with time according to the equation $y = a \sin \omega t$, where $a = 0.015$ m and $\omega = 6\pi$ rad s^{-1}. A particle B, 16 mm to the right of A, vibrates with the same frequency but lags behind particle A by $4\pi/5$ rad. Use this data to find

(a) the distance between extreme positions of particle A,
(b) the direction of propagation of the wave,
(c) the wavelength,
(d) the speed of the wave.

(objective 11)

Compare the time you took to complete this chapter with the recommended time. Are you keeping up to schedule?

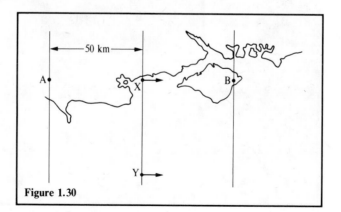

Figure 1.30

Chapter

2

Sound waves

Aim

In this chapter you will study the properties of sound waves and carry out experiments to determine the speed of sound in air. The ideas developed will be used to explain the phenomenon of beats and the Doppler effect.

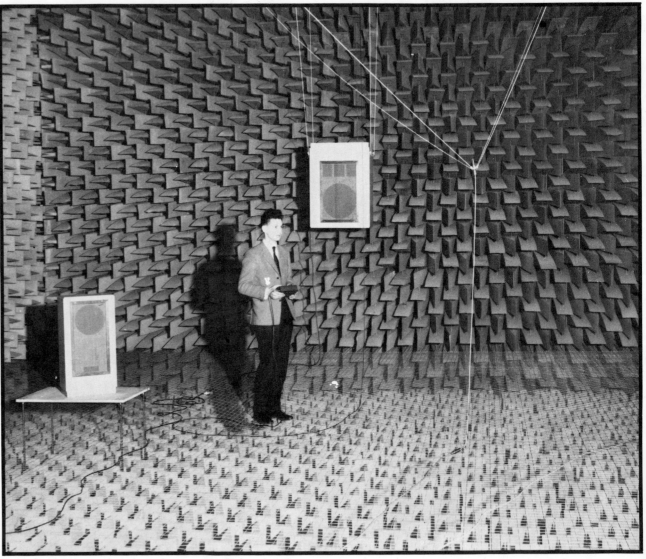

Investigating sound waves in an anechoic chamber.

Chapter 2

Study time: 1 week

Objectives

When you have completed the work in this chapter you should be able to:

1 Use the following scientific terms correctly: compression, rarefaction, beats.

2 Explain, in terms of pressure variation and particle displacement, how a sound wave is propagated.

3 Draw and interpret diagrams which represent the variation of pressure and of particle displacement with time.

4 Recall the speed of sound in air at 0°C.

5 Recall the factors which affect the speed of sound in air.

6 Describe and explain an experiment to determine the speed of sound in air.

7 Describe and explain the reflection, refraction and interference of sound waves.

8 Explain how beats are produced, and recall and use the equation for beat frequency.

9 EXTENSION
Explain what is meant by the Doppler effect.

10 EXTENSION
Derive and use expressions for the change in frequency of a wave motion when
(a) the source is moving relative to a fixed observer, and
(b) the observer is moving relative to a fixed source.

11 EXTENSION
Outline a practical application of the Doppler effect.

Experiments in chapter 2

WP 3 Speed of sound in air
($\frac{3}{4}$ hour)
WP 4 Interference of sound waves
(1 hour)

References

Akrill   Chapters 18 and 19
Duncan FWA   Chapter 7
Nelkon   Chapters 24 and 29
Whelan   Chapters 14, 15 and 41

2.1 Analysing sound waves

Sounds originate from vibrating sources. Sound energy can be transmitted through gases, as well as solids and liquids, but not through a vacuum. Sound is transmitted as a longitudinal progressive wave. As you observed using a slinky in experiment WP1, periodic longitudinal waves produce a series of compressions and rarefactions, travelling through the medium, which enable energy to be transmitted from source to receiver. Sound waves cause the ear-drum to vibrate and impulses are sent to the brain producing the sensation which we call 'sound'.

Sound waves are distinguished from other longitudinal waves by being *audible*. Sound waves are longitudinal progressive waves with frequencies between 20 Hz and 20 kHz. Audible frequency limits vary slightly for different people, and the upper frequency limit decreases with age. You can find your own audible frequency range by connecting a loudspeaker to a signal generator and varying the frequency up to 30 kHz.

Longitudinal progressive waves with frequencies above 20 kHz are called *ultrasonic* waves. Ultrasonic waves and sound waves travel at the same speed. In air this speed is about 330 m s^{-1}. (The prefix *ultra* indicates 'higher than audible frequency', and must not be confused with the prefix *super* which is used in supersonic to indicate 'speeds greater than the speed of sound'.)

Ultrasonic waves with frequencies as high as 6×10^8 Hz can be produced in a quartz crystal, using the piezo-electric effect (this effect causes a crystal to alternately shrink or expand when an alternating electric field is applied to it).

Background reading
Griffiths, D.R. *Echoes of bats and men.*

Q 2.1 Self-assessment question
(a) What are the approximate wavelengths of the highest and lowest frequency sound waves?
(b) What is the wavelength of waves produced by an ultrasonic vibrator of frequency 10^8 Hz?■

Representing sound waves

Figure 2.1a shows layers of particles in a medium in their undisturbed positions, and when displaced to new positions by the passage of a compression wave through the medium. Figure 2.1b shows the variation in particle displacement at different points in the medium. Particle displacement to the right is shown as positive displacement (upwards, on the graph).

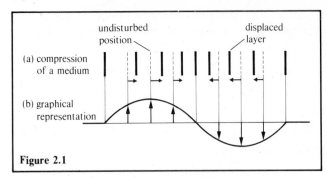

Figure 2.1

We can observe particle displacement when a transverse wave travels along a spring; observing particle displacement when a longitudinal wave passes through air is much more difficult. The following exercise will help you to visualise the displacements which occur.

1 Cut a slit 2 mm wide and 90 mm long in a 100 mm $\times$ 150 mm card (or fasten two cards edge-to-edge with a 2 mm gap).
2 Place the card over figure 2.2 with the slit at the top of the diagram.
3 Move the card downward with a constant velocity. The parts of the sine curves that you see through the slit correspond to a row of particles along which a longitudinal wave is travelling. You should notice that each

particle oscillates about its equilibrium position (it executes simple harmonic motion). All the particles have a similar motion, but within a wavelength each has a different phase, and regions of compression and rarefaction travel from left to right with constant velocity.

Figure 2.2

Detectors of sound, like microphones, respond to the pressure variations which occur in the medium. It is therefore important to represent sound waves in terms of these pressure variations.

Q 2.2 Development question*

Figure 2.3 shows a graph of particle displacement y against distance x at a particular instant of time.

(a) In which regions have particles of the medium been displaced to the left, and in which to the right?

(b) At which points will the pressure be maximum (compression)?

(c) At which points will the pressure be minimum (rarefaction)?

(d) Where is the pressure normal?

(e) Sketch a graph of the pressure change Δp against distance x at the instant shown, marking in the points A–F.■

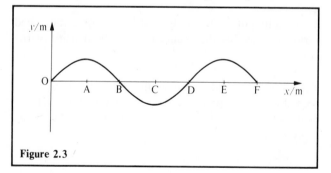

Figure 2.3

The points of maximum pressure and maximum particle displacement do not coincide. The pressure is maximum or minimum where the displacement is zero. When the progressive wave is sinusoidal, the pressure curve has the same shape as the displacement curve, but is displaced by a quarter of a wavelength.

Atmospheric pressure is about 10^5 N m^{-2} (Pa) and the wavelength of sound in air is about 1 m. For the loudest sound that we can tolerate, the pressure variation is approximately 30 Pa and the particle displacement about 10^{-5} m. For the faintest sound that we can hear, the corresponding figures are 2×10^{-5} Pa and 10^{-11} m. The particle displacement for quiet sounds is therefore smaller than the wavelength of light (5×10^{-7} m), and for the very faintest of sounds it is even smaller than the diameter of an atom (10^{-10} m).

2.2 The speed of sound waves

The first attempts to measure the speed of sound in air directly were made in the sixteenth century. The basis of these methods was to measure the time interval which elapsed between seeing the flash of a distant gun and hearing the report. Two contemporaries of Newton, the astronomers Flamsteed and Halley, measured the speed of sound between Greenwich Observatory and Shooters Hill, obtaining a value of 1142 feet per second (348 m s⁻¹).

Q 2.3 Self-assessment question
What were the main sources of error in this type of experiment?■

Now, because refined and accurate methods of timing are available, you can measure the speed of sound directly by recording the transit time of sound waves over a very short distance of about 1 metre. (Later, in the unit *Vibrations and waves*, the speed of sound will be found indirectly by measuring the wavelength of a wave of known frequency).

E Experiment WP3
Speed of sound in air
The aim of this experiment is to obtain a value for the speed of sound in air by a direct method, using an oscilloscope.

Factors affecting the speed of sound

In 1862 Regnault, a French physicist, made use of the gas and water pipes which were being laid in Paris to conduct a long series of experiments on the propagation of sound in pipes. For measuring time intervals he used a revolving drum, on which the instant at which a pistol was fired was electrically recorded. The arrival of the sound at the other end of the pipe moved a diaphragm, closing a circuit and recording this instant also on the drum. By using successive reflections from the ends of the pipes, the sound could be made to travel through distances up to 20 000 metres. To investigate some of the factors which might affect the speed of sound, he measured it at different pressures and in different gases and corrected his results for temperature and humidity. As a result of this, he reached two important conclusions.

1 The speed is independent of the pressure, at a fixed temperature.

2 In different gases, at the same pressure, the speed varies inversely as the square root of the density of the gas.

These experimental results supported the theoretical prediction of the mathematician Laplace who, in 1816, proposed that the speed of a longitudinal wave in a gas is given by

$$c = \sqrt{\frac{\gamma p}{\rho}},$$

where p is the pressure of the gas, ρ the density, and γ is a dimensionless constant (the ratio of the specific heats of the gas: this is covered in the unit *Thermal properties*).

Q 2.4 Self-assessment question
(a) What happens to the volume occupied by a given mass of gas when the pressure is halved, but the temperature remains constant?

(b) What happens to the gas density ρ in this case?

(c) What happens to the ratio p/ρ, and therefore to the speed of sound in a gas, when the pressure changes at constant temperature?■

How does the speed of sound depend on temperature? Both pressure and density may be affected if the temperature of a gas changes. The gas laws (introduced in the unit *Structure of matter*) summarise the relationship between the pressure p, volume V and absolute temperature T, for a fixed mass m of a gas, in the equation

$$pV = kT,$$

where k is a constant.

If the density of the gas is ρ ($\rho = m/V$), then $V = m/\rho$.

Therefore $p\left(\dfrac{m}{\rho}\right) = kT,$

$$\frac{p}{\rho} = \frac{kT}{m}.$$

The speed of sound $c = \sqrt{\dfrac{\gamma p}{\rho}},$

therefore $c = \sqrt{\dfrac{\gamma kT}{m}},$

or $c \propto \sqrt{T}.$

The speed of sound is therefore proportional to the square root of the absolute temperature.

Q **2.5 Self-assessment question**
For air at standard temperature and pressure (s.t.p.), the density is 1.3 kg m^{-3}, the pressure is 1.0×10^5 Pa, and γ is equal to 1.4. Calculate a value for the speed of sound in air.■

Q **2.6 Self-assessment question**
The speed of sound in air at 0°C is 330.0 m s^{-1}. What is the change in speed per °C rise in temperature?■

Q **2.7 Study question**
Discuss qualitatively how the speed of sound depends upon the humidity of the air.■

Q **2.8 Self-assessment question**
Deep-sea divers breathe a mixture of helium and oxygen to prevent nitrogen being dissolved in the blood (helium is insoluble). What frequency is heard if a man, who produces a note of 256 Hz (middle C) in air, fills his lungs with helium at atmospheric pressure and tries to produce the same note? (Assume that the wavelength of the sound waves is unchanged. Density of air $\rho_a = 1.3$ kg m^{-3}, density of helium $\rho_h = 0.18$ kg m^{-3}, γ_a for air = 1.4, γ_h for helium, = 1.6.)■

2.3 Properties of sound waves

Reflection
When sound waves impinge on hard surfaces, most of the energy is reflected back, obeying the laws of reflection. At soft or porous surfaces, much of the wave energy is absorbed. If the reflecting surface is a long way from the observer, the reflected sound arrives some time after the waves travelling directly to the observer, and an echo is heard. The echo seems to be coming from another source: the virtual image formed by reflection. Echoes are useful for measuring sea depth (sonar depth finding), and the interior of the body can be investigated by obtaining echoes of ultrasonic waves.

In a large hall there are many reflecting surfaces close to an observer. The direct sound and the reflected sound cannot be distinguished, giving the impression that the original sound has been prolonged. It slowly fades away, as energy is absorbed in successive reflections. This effect is called *reverberation*, and the quality of the sound we hear is affected by these multiple reflections.

Background reading
'Ultrasound in medical diagnosis', by G.B. Davey and P.N.T. Wells, *Scientific American*, May 1978.

Q **2.9 Self-assessment question**
How can you account for the fact that a 'rough' cliff face can produce a distinct sound image (an echo), whereas a highly polished surface is needed to produce a clear image when light is reflected?■

Refraction
Sound waves can be refracted. Sound travels more rapidly in warm air than in cooler air. During the day the upper layers of the air are cooler than the layers nearer the earth, whilst at night the opposite is true.

Q **2.10 Study question**
(a) Explain why sounds carry over long distances on a still, frosty night.
(b) Why does a hot still day seem quiet?
(c) How would you set up a ripple tank analogue of the situation described in (a)?■

The speed of sound waves is increased, relative to a stationary observer, if the whole mass of air carrying the compressions is being blown towards him. We are all familiar with the difficulty of getting our voices to carry when we shout into the wind. The sound cannot be 'blown back', since sound travels ten times faster than a gale force wind. The wind is producing refraction. This is because the wind speed is always low near the ground and increases with height.

Q **2.11 Self-assessment question**
Explain, with the aid of diagrams, how the direction of the wind affects audibility on the ground.■

Comprehension exercise

SOMERSET BUMPS

A team from Bristol University has announced that the distinctive noises, locally known as 'Somerset bumps', which have been heard regularly in the South West of England for several months were caused by refraction of shockwaves from Paris or Heathrow-bound flights of Concorde.

An aircraft travelling at supersonic speed has a primary 'boom carpet' where the characteristic 'double bang' will be heard. This carpet is the area reached by downward travelling shockwaves and its size is determined by upwards refraction of these waves (figure 2.4). In the upper atmosphere, where supersonic aircraft fly, steady winds lead to downward refraction of the upward shockwaves from an aircraft moving in the same direction as the wind, giving a secondary 'carpet'. In addition a tertiary 'carpet' may be caused by downward refraction of reflected primary shockwaves. (Reflection occurs from 'smooth' surfaces such as the sea or deserts; on land the waves are scattered.)

Concorde's flight paths are such that its primary 'boom carpets' are over the sea. The secondary and tertiary effects cause the 'bumps'. Over the West Country the upper atmospheric winds may blow in the same direction for weeks on end and this has led to the regular occurrence of the sounds with incoming flights. The wind direction, which is seasonal, should change in spring and 'bumps' will be caused by outward flights.

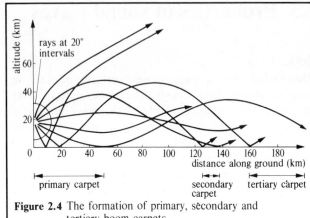

Figure 2.4 The formation of primary, secondary and tertiary boom carpets

Questions

1 What is the direction of the wind producing the refraction effects shown in figure 2.4?

2 What effect will an increase in wind speed have on the position of the secondary 'carpets'?

3 Suggest why some sound waves are shown travelling without being refracted.

4 Sketch possible paths for the sound waves from Concorde on the other side of the aircraft.

Interference

Sound waves can exhibit the phenomenon of interference. This can be observed by connecting two loudspeakers in parallel to a signal generator so that they oscillate in phase. The result of the superposition of the waves can be detected with a microphone and c.r.o., or by listening.

E Experiment WP 4
Interference of sound waves
In this experiment you will investigate a sound interference pattern and obtain data from which you can estimate the wavelength of sound waves and calculate the speed of sound in air.

Q 2.12 Self-assessment question
What will be the effect on a sound wave interference pattern if
(a) the pitch of both loudspeakers is lowered,
(b) the connections to one of the loudspeakers are reversed so that the two speakers oscillate out of phase.
Give reasons for your answers.■

EXTENSION

Q 2.13 Study question
Make brief notes on *either* Quinke's *or* Hebb's method for determining the speed of sound. In both these methods the phenomenon of interference is used to measure the wavelength of sound waves.■

Beats

This effect is another example of superposition. It occurs when two waves of similar amplitudes but slightly different frequencies are superposed. The result is a periodic rise and fall in loudness.

WP 3 Large transparencies
Beats

Two waves of different frequencies are superposed, using the transparencies, to produce a variable amplitude wave.

Q 2.14 Study question
(a) Explain, with the help of a diagram, how beats are produced.
(b) What is meant by the term beat period?
(c) Derive an expression relating the beat frequency to the frequencies of the two superposed waves.
(d) How can beats be used to measure an unknown frequency? ∎

Q 2.15 Self-assessment question
A piano tuner sounds a calibrated tuning fork for middle C (256 Hz) at the same time as the middle C of the piano he is tuning. He hears beats of frequency 4 Hz.
(a) What are the possible frequencies of the piano string?
(b) What must he do to tune the string, and how will he know when it is in tune? ∎

EXTENSION

Q 2.16 Study question
Derive mathematically an expression for the total displacement of a layer of air due to the superposition of two waves with equations

$$y_1 = a \sin \omega_1 t \quad \text{and} \quad y_2 = a \sin(\omega_2 t + \phi).$$

From this show that the beat frequency is given by

$$2\pi f = \omega_1 - \omega_2 \quad \text{or} \quad f = f_1 - f_2. \blacksquare$$

SYLLABUS EXTENSION

2.4 The Doppler effect

The pitch of the note from a siren, of an ambulance or a fire engine, appears to change as it passes you. This apparent change in frequency is called the Doppler effect, and is due to the relative movement of source and observer. The effect is produced by a change in wavelength.

Moving source

Figure 2.5 represents wavecrests from a moving source. Successive positions of the source are represented by points S_1 to S_4. Wavefront 1 was emitted when the source was at S_1, wavefront 2 originated from point S_2, and so on. The wavefronts moving towards O are compressed, the wavefronts moving towards O_1 are spread out. However, the speed of the waves, c, is unchanged. It is not affected by the speed of the source, since the wave speed is a property of the medium (and the waves forget about the source as soon as they leave it).

Q 2.17 Development question
Source S travels with speed v_s towards O and produces sound waves of frequency f_s and wave speed c.
(a) How far does the source travel in one second?
(b) How many wavefronts are produced in one second?
(c) What is the distance into which this one-second-wavetrain travelling to O is packed?

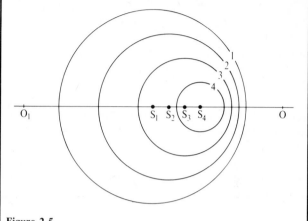

Figure 2.5

(d) Show that the decreased wavelength at O, λ_o, is given by

$$\lambda_o = \frac{c - v_s}{f_s}.$$

(e) The observed frequency, f_o, is the number of wavelengths travelling past the observer in one second. Express f_o in terms of c and λ_o.

(f) Show that $f_o = \left(\dfrac{c}{c - v_s} \right) f_s$.

(g) Show that, for an observer at O_1, the observed frequency is

$$\left(\frac{c}{c + v_s} \right) f_s. \blacksquare$$

2.18 Self-assessment question

A source emitting a note of frequency 600 Hz approaches a stationary observer at a constant velocity of one-fifth of the speed of sound in air, and passes him. Calculate the observed change in frequency as the source passes the observer.■

Suppose the source is moving along XY (figure 2.6) with a velocity v_s while the observer is stationary at O. When the source is at P, it is moving towards O with a component velocity along PO of $v_s \cos \theta$. It is this component of the velocity which determines the frequency heard at O.

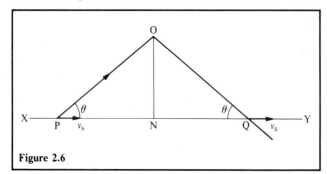

Figure 2.6

2.19 Self-assessment question

Write down an expression for the apparent frequency f_o, in terms of the emitted frequency f_s, when the body is at
(a) point P,
(b) point N,
(c) point Q.■

2.20 Self-assessment question

An observer's perpendicular distance from a point N on a railway track is 50 m. An express train moves along the track at a steady speed of 60 m s^{-1}, continuously sounding a whistle of frequency 500 Hz. The speed of sound in air is 340 m s^{-1}.
(a) What is the frequency heard by the observer when the distance x of the approaching train from the point N is (i) 200 m, (ii) 100 m, (iii) 50 m, (iv) 20 m and (v) 0?
(b) Draw a graph to show how the frequency heard by the observer varies with the distance of the train from the point N, for both positive (train approaching) and negative (train receding) values of x.
(c) Sketch, using the same axes, the curve that would be obtained if the observer was closer to the track.■

Moving observer

In this case the wavelength λ is unchanged, but the movement of the observer affects the number of wavecrests received per second by the observer.

2.21 Development question

If the source has an emitted frequency of f_s, a stationary observer receives f_s wavecrests per second.
(a) Express f_s in terms of λ and c.
(b) If the observer moves towards the source with speed v_o, how many extra wavecrests are received per second?
(c) The apparent frequency f_o is the total number of wavecrests received per second by the moving observer. Write down an expression for f_o.

(d) Hence show that $f_o = \left(\dfrac{c + v_o}{c} \right) f_s$.

(e) If the observer moves away from the source, show that

$$f_o = \left(\frac{c - v_o}{c} \right) f_s.■$$

The relationships between the observed, or apparent, frequency f_o and the emitted frequency f_s can be summarised as follows.
For a moving source:

$$\frac{f_o}{f_s} = \frac{\text{velocity of waves relative to the medium}}{\text{velocity of waves relative to the source}}.$$

For a moving observer:

$$\frac{f_o}{f_s} = \frac{\text{velocity of waves relative to the observer}}{\text{velocity of waves relative to the medium}}.$$

The equations can be combined if both source and observer are moving relative to the medium.

Notes
1   In deriving the preceding equations, the velocities v_s, v_o and c were all assumed to be measured relative to the air or, more generally, to the medium in which the wave travels.
2   The Doppler effect occurs with electromagnetic waves. In this case there is no medium relative to which a velocity can be defined, and we can speak only of the relative velocity of the source and receiver.
3   The equations derived for sound waves can be used for electromagnetic waves if v_s and/or v_o is much less than c (3×10^8 m s^{-1} for e.m. waves). If v_o or v_s become comparable to c, different equations are needed.

Applications of the Doppler effect

Q **2.22 Self-assessment question**
(a) A source of sound emits a note of frequency 1000 Hz. Suppose that the source moves at the speed of sound, c, directly towards a stationary observer. Calculate the frequency of the note heard by the observer (i) as the source approaches, (ii) as the source recedes.
(b) If the source is stationary, and the observer moves directly towards the source with velocity c, calculate the frequency of the note heard by the observer (i) as he approaches the source, (ii) as he recedes from the source.
(c) Comment on your results.■

Q **2.23 Self-assessment question**
A car, sounding its horn, moves away from a stationary observer at a steady speed of 5 m s⁻¹ towards a plane reflecting wall. The frequency of the note emitted by the horn is 400 Hz, and the speed of sound in air is 340 m s⁻¹. What is the frequency of the beats heard by the observer?■

The Doppler effect for electromagnetic waves can be used in tracking an artificial satellite (figure 2.7). The satellite emits a radio signal of constant frequency f_s. The signal received on the ground from the satellite is combined with a constant signal, also of frequency f_s, generated in the receiver. This gives rise to beats.

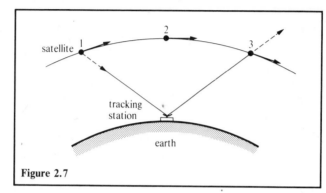

Figure 2.7

Q **2.24 Self-assessment question**
(a) What happens to the beat frequency Δf as the satellite moves from position 1 to position 3?
(b) If v_s is the component of the satellite's velocity towards the receiving station, show that

$$\frac{\Delta f}{f_s} \approx \frac{v_s}{c}.$$

(Assume that Δf is small, and f_o is therefore approximately equal to f_s.)■

A similar technique, using the Doppler effect and beats, is employed to detect the movement or measure the speed of a reflecting surface. Emitter and receiver are placed together near the moving surface. Waves reflected back to the source from an approaching target surface will have an increased frequency. This changed frequency is mixed with the original emitted frequency to obtain the beat frequency, which depends on the speed of the reflecting surface.

Q **2.25 Study question**
If a reflecting surface travels towards a stationary emitter/receiver with speed v, show that the detected change in frequency, Δf, is given by

$$\Delta f \approx \left(\frac{2v}{c}\right) f_s,$$

where f_s is the emitted frequency. (Hint: consider the moving reflector as a moving 'observer' receiving waves from a stationary source, and then as a moving 'source' emitting to a stationary receiver.)■

The Doppler-shift frequency Δf can be used to detect a foetal heart beat, if ultrasonic waves are reflected from the moving surface of the heart. The ultrasonic frequency can be adjusted to produce a value of Δf which is in the audible range, producing sound in the detector earphones. Waves reflected from stationary structures in the body will undergo no Doppler shift and the observer will hear nothing. Reflections from a beating heart will produce a varying tone in the earphones.

Speed detectors used by police measure car speeds using the Doppler-shift frequency with electromagnetic waves (radar).

Q 2.26 Self-assessment question

Microwaves of wavelength 100 mm are transmitted from a source so as to strike a car which is approaching the source. The reflected wave is found to give a beat frequency of 200 Hz when superposed on the transmitted wave. The speed of electromagnetic waves is 3×10^8 m s^{-1}. Calculate the speed of the approaching car. ■

The Doppler effect for light waves is important in astronomy. Analysis of the spectra of light from distant stars shows shifts in the frequency of spectral lines compared to spectra from the same elements on earth. These can be interpreted as Doppler shifts due to the motion of the stars. For a star travelling away from the observer with speed v, $\Delta f/f = v/c$.

Questions on objectives

1 Figure 2.8 represents a longitudinal progressive wave. Which of the distances marked (A–E) is
(a) the amplitude of the wave,
(b) the wavelength of the wave?

(*objective* 2)

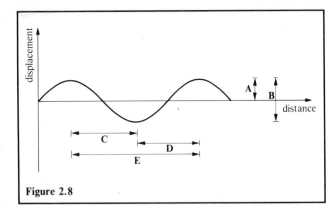

Figure 2.8

2 When a guitar string is plucked, a musical note is produced. Describe the sequence of changes by which energy from the string reaches the ear.

(*objective* 6)

3 The speed of sound in air, c, is given by the expression

$$c = \sqrt{\frac{\gamma p}{\rho}}.$$

(a) What do the symbols in this equation represent?
(b) What is the effect on the speed of sound in air of a change in pressure?
(c) How does the speed of sound in air depend upon the temperature?

(*objective* 5)

4 When two musical notes of slightly different frequencies are sounded together, a listener is aware of a kind of throbbing: a periodic rise and fall in the loudness of the sound.
(a) What name is given to this phenomenon?
(b) Explain this observation qualitatively, in terms of the principle of superposition of waves.

(*objective* 8)

5 An accurately calibrated tuning fork of frequency 320 Hz is sounded with the note D of a piano and a beat frequency of 2 Hz is heard. What are the possible frequencies of the piano string?

(*objective* 8)

6 The apparatus illustrated in figure 2.9 shows a possible method of measuring the speed of sound in air. Sound from a loudspeaker is passed through a system of tubing, and reaches a detector by two paths, A and B. The length of path B can be varied by moving the sliding tube.

(a) When the sliding tube is moved, the intensity of the sound varies from a minimum to a maximum, to a minimum again, and so on. Explain this.

(b) In a particular experiment the tube was moved a distance of 68 mm between successive minima of sound. The frequency of the source was 2500 Hz. Calculate a value for the speed of sound.

(*objectives 6 and 7*)

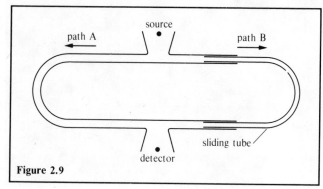

Figure 2.9

7 Two loudspeakers X and Y are connected in parallel to an audio-frequency oscillator (signal generator). An observer at a point O, which is equidistant from X and Y, detects a sound of maximum intensity. As the observer moves parallel to XY the intensity decreases, and first falls to a minimum at a point P. The distances PX and PY are measured and found to be 0.50 m and 0.35 m respectively.

(a) Calculate the wavelength of the sound waves.

(b) Calculate the speed of sound in air, if the frequency of the source is 1.14 kHz.

(*objective 7*)

8 EXTENSION

Derive an expression for the frequency f_o recorded by a stationary observer when a source of frequency f_s approaches him at constant speed v_s.

(*objective 10*)

9 EXTENSION

A police car travelling at a speed of 34 m s^{-1} passes a stationary observer. The police car siren emits a note of frequency 450 Hz. Calculate the apparent change in frequency of the note as the police car approaches the observer and passes him. The speed of sound in air is 340 m s^{-1}.

(*objective 10*)

Chapter 3

Light waves

Aim

In this chapter you will consider how two rival theories about the nature of light, the corpuscular theory of Newton and the wave theory of Huygens, explained the phenomena of reflection, refraction and dispersion. Interference of light, which provides direct evidence that light has wave properties, will be studied experimentally.

Chapter 3

Objectives

When you have completed the work in this chapter, you should be able to:

1 Use the following scientific terms correctly: monochromatic, path difference, secondary wavelets.

2 Recall the approximate wavelength of light waves.

3 State Huygens' hypothesis. Explain how it is used in constructing reflected and refracted wavefronts, and show how this construction is in agreement with the laws of reflection and refraction.

4 State the conditions required to produce a steady interference pattern using light waves.

5 Perform and describe an experiment to determine the wavelength of light, using Young's method.

6 Derive, for the double slit experiment, an expression for the wavelength in terms of slit separation d, fringe separation x and distance D from slit sources to fringe pattern.

7 Solve problems involving relationships between phase difference and path difference, including the analysis of interference patterns.

8 EXTENSION
Outline briefly the historical development of methods for measuring the velocity of light and describe one accurate determination.

9 EXTENSION
Explain how the wavelength of light can be measured using Fresnel's biprism.

References

Akrill	Chapter 19
Bolton	Chapter 6
Duncan FWA	Chapter 8
Nelkon	Chapters 25 and 26
Wenham	Chapter 23
Whelan	Chapters 14, 37 and 38

Experiments in chapter 3

WP5 Observing double slit interference
($1\frac{1}{2}$ hours, but ten minutes preparation work is required a few hours before the experiment.)

Study time: $1\frac{1}{2}$ weeks

3.1 Introduction

What is light? What is vision? It is hard for us to realise that in the days of ancient Greece, and even much later, the question debated was whether we see because something enters our eyes from objects (Aristotle's view) or whether our eyes send out a stream of something which collides with an object to make it visible (Plato's view). It was only at the beginning of the seventeenth century that light was accepted as something emitted by luminous objects. The great debate then was about the nature of this emission. Two theories of light were proposed: the corpuscular theory of Newton and the wave theory of Huygens. In the following two sections we consider the way in which these theories attempted to provide explanations about the behaviour of light.

3.2 The corpuscular theory

In his famous book 'Opticks', published in 1704, Isaac Newton proposed that light rays were streams of very small bodies (corpuscles) emitted from shining substances. He could not support the idea that light was waves, because he observed that light clearly travels in straight lines and produces sharp shadows: '. . . waves on the surface of still water passing by the sides of a broad obstacle which stops part of them bend afterwards and spread gradually into the quiet water behind the obstacle. The waves . . . , wherein sounds consist, bend manifestly though not so much as the waves of water. . . . Light is never known to follow crooked passages nor to bend into the shadow. . . .'

Newton did not merely propose a theory but produced much experimental evidence, much of it never reported before, and in each case his theory was offered as an explanation. These experiments included his investigation of the dispersion of white light into a spectrum and interference effects in thin films (Newton's rings). The way light was reflected suggested to Newton an elastic collision between corpuscles and the reflecting medium. Refraction he explained as follows: that bodies refract light by acting upon its rays in lines perpendicular to their surface. He concluded that at a refracting boundary the motion (speed or momentum) perpendicular to the boundary would be altered whilst the motion of the ray parallel to the boundary would be unchanged.

Q **3.1 Study question**
(a) Explain briefly, with a diagram, how the refraction of a ray of light incident at angle i_1 at an air – glass boundary is explained by the corpuscular theory. Deduce an equation for the ratio of the speeds in the two media in terms of the angles in your diagram.
(b) What might Newton conclude, from his experiments on dispersion in a prism, about the relative speeds of red and blue rays of light in glass? ■

Newton studied the concentric dark and bright rings formed when light was reflected or transmitted in a thin film of air between a curved lens surface and a flat glass surface. He even observed diffraction effects due to a hair, but though he observed diffraction fringes and a broadening of the shadow, every observation was explained to his own satisfaction in terms of the interaction between the corpuscles of light and matter. One of the strongest reasons why Newton rejected the wave theory was his belief that waves required a medium in which to travel, and light seemed to travel through space without a medium. Newton made a unique contribution to the study of the nature of light, by providing a lot of new experimental evidence, and he identified the key questions even though many of his answers were rejected by later scientists in favour of an explanation in terms of a wave model.

One key question was the possibility of interaction between light and matter, a factor neglected by many scientists in the eighteenth and nineteenth centuries. Twentieth century studies of such interactions have led to the development of a wave – particle theory of light.

3.3 Huygens' theory

Christiaan Huygens published his 'Treatise on light' in 1690. In this he proposed that light: '. . . spreads, as sound does, by spherical surfaces and waves: for I will call them waves from their resemblance to those which are seen to be formed in water when a stone is thrown into it . . .' One of his main arguments was that rays of light are observed to pass through each other. He could not imagine streams of particles doing this, but he did believe that waves could, because this happened also with sound waves. Huygens was impressed by the similarities between sound and light, and found it necessary to introduce the idea of a medium ('etheral matter') between earth and sun to transmit light waves. He explored the idea of light being similar to water waves, to explain both reflection and refraction.

Huygens' hypothesis states that every point on an existing wavefront can be considered as a source of secondary wavelets which radiate out with the wave velocity.

Huygens' construction applies this statement as follows: from a given position of the wavefront, a later position can be constructed by drawing the envelope of all the secondary wavelets (figure 3.1).

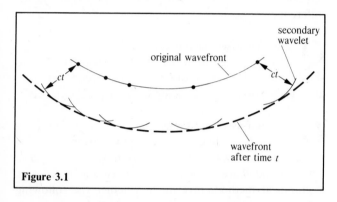

Figure 3.1

The effect produced at some point ahead of the wave (the amplitude of the disturbance) must be the result of super-posing (adding up the amplitudes of) all the secondary wavelets. (This process will be used in the unit *Vibrations and waves* to explain diffraction effects.)

Note. Huygens assumed, without providing explanation, that there was no backwards propagation of waves from the secondary wavelets. Later Fresnel showed that the construction agreed with observations if it was assumed that the amplitude of the secondary wavelets varied from maximum in the forward direction to zero in the back-wards direction. Hence in constructing new wavefronts only a small forward arc is drawn.

Reflection

Q **3.2 Study question**

In figure 3.2, AB is a wavefront approaching a reflecting surface at speed c. The angle of incidence is i. A secondary wavelet from B travels to B_1 in time t.
(a) Sketch the diagram and use Huygens' construction to determine the position of the reflected wavefront after time t. Show that the angles of incidence and reflection are equal.
(b) Sketch the wavefront a time $2t/3$ after it has left the position AB.■

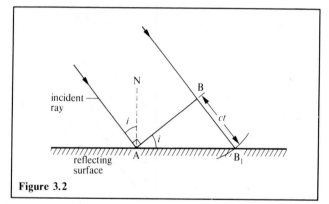

Figure 3.2

Refraction

Q **3.3 Study question**

In figure 3.3, AB is a wavefront approaching a boundary between two media. The angle of incidence is i_1. A secondary wavelet from B travels to B_1 in time t at speed c_1. The wavespeed is c_2 in the second medium.
(a) Sketch the diagram and, assuming that $c_2 = 2c_1/3$, construct the refracted wavefront A_1B_1. If this is at an angle i_2 with the boundary, show that

$$\frac{c_1}{c_2} = \frac{\sin i_1}{\sin i_2}.$$

(b) How does this equation differ from that you obtained in question 3.1a?
(c) Do measurements of the speed of light in different media support a wave or a particle theory of light?■

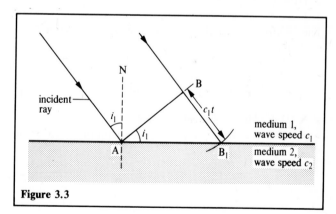

Figure 3.3

Snell's law of refraction, formulated from experiment in 1626, holds for light and for other wave motions. It states that, for waves of a given frequency,

$$\frac{\sin i_1}{\sin i_2} = \text{a constant, for two given media.}$$

Wave theory shows that this constant is the ratio of the wave speeds in the two media (c_1/c_2). This ratio is called the *refractive index* for waves travelling from medium 1 to medium 2.

The *absolute* refractive index n of a medium for a particular frequency is defined as:

$$n = \frac{\text{speed of light in vacuum}}{\text{speed of light in medium}} = \frac{c}{c_n}.$$

The refractive index of air at s.t.p. is 1.003, which is usually taken as 1.

The *relative* refractive index $_1n_2$ for waves passing from medium 1 to medium 2 is defined as:

$$_1n_2 = \frac{\text{speed of light in medium 1}}{\text{speed of light in medium 2}} = \frac{c_1}{c_2}.$$

Q **3.4 Self-assessment question**
Use the above notation and definitions to show that

$$_1n_2 = \frac{n_2}{n_1} \quad \text{and} \quad _2n_1 = \frac{1}{_1n_2}. \blacksquare$$

Q **3.5 Self-assessment question**
Figure 3.4 shows a wavefront refracted at a boundary between two media.
(a) Estimate the refractive index $_1n_2$.
(b) How will the waves emerge from medium 2? ■

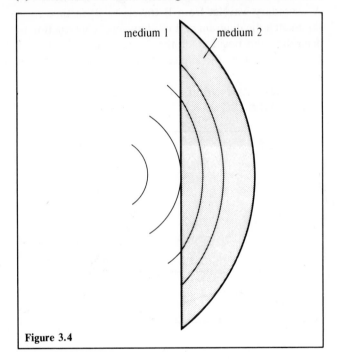

medium 1   medium 2

Figure 3.4

Dispersion

Refractive index has been defined for a particular medium and wave frequency because, as we saw earlier, wave speed in a medium often depends on frequency. In this case the medium is a dispersive medium. Glass, for example, disperses white light into its constituent colours. The colour of light is determined by the frequency of the radiation, so the refractive index of glass is different for different colours.

Q **3.6 Self-assessment question**
Draw a diagram, using Huygens' construction, to show how a plane wave of white light is refracted at an air – glass boundary, assuming $c_{\text{red}} > c_{\text{blue}}$ in glass. ■

Q **3.7 Self-assessment question**
It has been suggested that the variation of refractive index n with wavelength λ is given by $n = A + B/\lambda$, where A and B are constants for a given material. Using a graphical method, investigate whether the following data fit the equation.

λ/nm	450	500	550	600	650
n	1.633	1.630	1.627	1.625	1.623

Hint: select the variables of your graph to obtain a straight line (section 10.3 of the Student's Handbook will help you). Do not attempt to make the origin (0, 0). ■

Wavefronts due to a moving source

Huygens' construction applies to all waves. For example, what kind of wavefront is produced by a source moving faster than the wave speed, such as a supersonic plane? When an aircraft is moving through the air, the compression produced by the leading surfaces and the rarefaction created behind the plane produce a shock wave which travels through the air with the speed of sound. You can use Huygens' construction to construct the shock wavefront produced by Concorde.

Q **3.8 Development question***
Suppose Concorde is travelling at twice the speed of sound ($2c$) and moves from A to E in a straight line in time t. We will construct the position of the wavefront when the aircraft is at E.
(a) Draw a line AE 8 cm long. What distance does this represent, in terms of c and t?
(b) Draw the wave front which radiated from A and has travelled for a time t since the aircraft left A.
(c) Mark point B, the position of the plane at a time $t/4$ after it left A. How long has the wave been travelling from B if the aircraft is now at E? Draw the wavefront which has radiated from B.
(d) Construct the wavefronts which have radiated from C and D, the positions of the aircraft $t/2$ and $t/4$ before its present position at E.
(e) Draw in the shock wavefront (the envelope of all the wavelets) and mark the direction of the energy flow.
(f) Describe the shape of the wavefront. What do you think is meant by the phrase 'a carpet of sonic boom'. Do you think more people, or less, would be affected by the sonic boom if the aircraft increased its speed to $2\frac{1}{2}$ times the speed of sound? Explain your answer. ∎

3.4 Interference of light

In the eighteenth century most scientists accepted Newton's corpuscular theory of light. He was a scientist of great prestige and he had provided explanations for his extensive observations on the behaviour of light. Huygens, by contrast, had furnished no new experimental evidence in support of his theory which, though accounting well for reflection and refraction, could not satisfactorily explain the straight line propagation of light. If the speed of light could have been measured in glass or water that would have provided the necessary support for one or other theory, but experimental techniques had to develop over 150 years before the speed of light in water was measured by Foucault in 1850. However, the crucial experimental work which decided in favour of a wave theory for light was performed by Thomas Young at the beginning of the nineteenth century.

His most famous experiment was the observation of fringes when light waves from the same source passed through two narrow parallel slits arranged close together. His results provided clear evidence that, under certain conditions, light plus light gave darkness. That is, destructive interference was occurring: an effect which could only be explained if light was a periodic wave. Light waves are constantly being superposed, but we only obtain a steady interference pattern under very special conditions. It required a genius like Thomas Young to realise the nature of the problem and provide a solution.

Conditions for producing a visible interference pattern

Interference is the effect produced by superposing waves from *coherent sources*. Interference effects are difficult to produce with light because it is difficult to obtain coherent sources, and the light waves have very small wavelengths.

Q **3.9 Development question***
(a) Are two dippers on the same vibrating bar coherent sources for a ripple tank?
(b) Under what conditions are two dippers on separate vibrating bars coherent?
(c) Are two flute players playing the *same* note coherent sources, and would they produce a steady sound interference pattern?
(d) What would happen to any pattern produced in (c) if one flute player stopped for breath and then started again?
(e) Are you likely to get a steady interference pattern from two flute-playing groups, even if they are all playing the same note? Explain. ∎

A light source may appear to be emitting a steady wave. In fact, the light is emitted as a multitude of wave pulses. Each pulse is produced when there is an energy change in an individual atom and each lasts about 10^{-8} s or a million vibrations. Any constant phase relationship between two *separate* light sources lasts for much less than 10^{-8} s. It is therefore quite impossible for two separate sources of light to produce a visible interference pattern, just as no sound interference pattern would be expected from two flute bands, even if they only took breaths every few seconds. It is also clear that light waves from different parts of the same source will not have a constant phase relationship.

To produce a steady interference pattern, light waves must be superposed at a point after travelling by different paths. However, they should have come originally from the *same point* of the *same source* and the superposed waves must originate from the *same wavepulse*. This means that the path difference must be less than the pulse length.

Summary
1 Two coherent light sources must be derived from the same point source or slit. (The laser is an exception to this, since it produces coherent light from atoms acting in unison. Two different parts of the laser beam can be used to produce steady interference.)
2 To obtain a clear and extensive pattern, the primary source should be monochromatic. Interference patterns can be observed with white light, but are less clear because they consist of several superimposed patterns produced by different frequencies.
3 The secondary sources should be very close together. This ensures that there is a region where the waves superpose, and that the fringe separation is large enough to be detected easily.
4 The interfering light waves must be unpolarised, or polarised in the same plane (see the unit *Vibrations and waves*).
5 The coherent wavetrains should have similar amplitudes.

There are two ways in which two coherent wavetrains can be produced from one source, by division of the *wavefront* or by division of the *amplitude*. In Young's experiment, coherent wavetrains are produced by division of the wavefront. (Interference by division of amplitude is covered in the unit *Vibrations and waves*.)

Young's double slit experiment

Figure 3.5 shows a plane perpendicular to the slits. The primary slit S is illuminated by monochromatic light. Light waves are diffracted through this slit to illuminate the secondary slits S_1 and S_2, which are arranged parallel to the primary slit.

Diffracted waves emerge from S_1 and S_2 and, since they originate from the same source, they have a constant phase relationship. The slits S_1 and S_2 must be very close together, so that the waves are diffracted enough to produce an area where the two waves are superposed. Interference effects can be observed anywhere in the region where superposition occurs, so there are many possible positions for the screen.

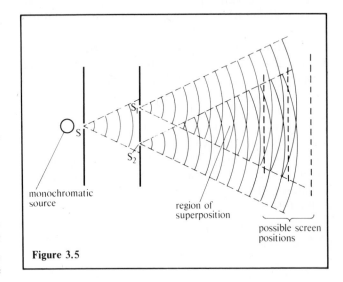

monochromatic source

region of superposition

possible screen positions

Figure 3.5

E Experiment WP5
Interference of light from two slits

In this experiment you will obtain an interference pattern, using Young's method, and estimate the wavelength of light.

Figure 3.6 indicates the geometry of a Young's double slit experiment. S_1 and S_2 represent coherent sources, in phase, and OM is the perpendicular bisector of S_1S_2. The diagram is *not* drawn to scale since, in this experiment, S_1S_2 is less than 1 mm, OM is about 1 m and OP is a few millimetres. There will be constructive interference at all points along line OM, because the path difference along this line is zero. At point O on the screen there will be maximum light (the zero order maximum). To find the effect at any other point P on the screen we must find the path difference at P.

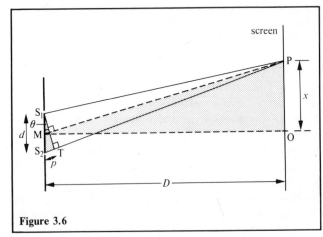

screen

Figure 3.6

Q 3.10 Development question*

(a) T is a point on the line S_2P such that $PT = PS_1$. What does the length TS_2 represent (note that it is equal to $PS_2 - PS_1$)?

(b) M is the midpoint of S_1S_2. Assuming that PM bisects line S_1T, why is PM perpendicular to S_1T?

(c) If the line S_1T is rotated through an angle θ, so that it lies along S_1S_2, where will line MP be?

(d) What is the value of angle PMO?

(e) Why is angle S_1TS_2 almost equal to $90°$?

(f) What does this imply about triangle TS_1S_2 and triangle OMP?

(g) From part (f), $TS_2/S_1S_2 = OP/PM$. Show how this leads to the equation $p = dx/D$.

(h) Some approximations have been made in obtaining this result. Why are these approximations justified?∎

Q 3.11 Development question

(a) The zero order bright fringe is at O. The first bright fringe is at a distance x_1 from O. What is the path difference for this fringe? Write an equation relating λ and x_1.

(b) If the second bright fringe is at a distance x_2 from O, write an equation relating λ and x_2.

(c) If the nth bright fringe is at a distance x_n from O, what is x_n in terms of λ?

(d) If the $(n + 1)$th bright fringe is at a distance x_{n+1} from O, what is x_{n+1} in terms of λ?

(e) What is the separation between the nth and the $(n + 1)$th bright fringes?

(f) Explain why the pattern on the screen looks like figure 3.7.∎

A double slit interference pattern for monochromatic light consists of equally spaced bright and dark fringes, parallel to the slits. They can be seen on a screen, or in an eyepiece, anywhere in the region where the waves are superposed (figure 3.5).

From an interference pattern similar to that shown in figure 3.7, the wavelength of light from a monochromatic source can be calculated, using

$$\text{wavelength} = \frac{\text{slit separation} \times \text{fringe separation}}{\text{distance from slits to fringes}},$$

$$\lambda = \frac{dx}{D}, \quad \text{if} \quad D \gg d.$$

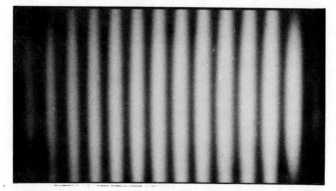

Figure 3.7

Q 3.12 Self-assessment question

A double slit interference pattern is produced using a monochromatic slit source and two slits 1.0 mm apart. The fringes are seen 1.20 m from the double slit. If the distance across twenty fringes is 14.2 mm, what is the wavelength of the light from the source?∎

Q 3.13 Self-assessment question

The equation $x = \lambda D/d$ is derived by assuming that D is very much larger than d. It is a useful approximate relationship, even when applied to the interference pattern in a ripple tank. From figure 1.22a calculate the wavelength from the interference pattern, using the formula, and compare this value with a direct measurement of wavelength from the photograph.∎

When observing a double slit interference pattern one can locate the minima more precisely than the maxima. The separation of adjacent minima is the same as the separation of adjacent maxima.

How bright is the screen at places between a maximum and a minimum? At these points the superposing waves are neither in phase nor completely out of phase. The amplitude of the resultant wave varies between maximum and minimum like a sine or cosine curve, so the brightness along the screen (which depends on the square of the amplitude) varies like a graph of $\cos^2\theta$, with a zero order maximum at the midpoint O of the pattern. Figure 3.8 shows a graph of relative light intensity I/I_0 against distance x along the screen from O when monochromatic light passes through two very narrow slits.

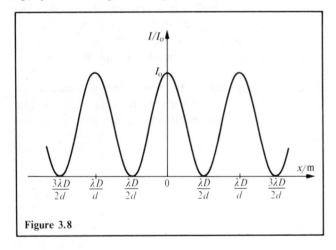

Figure 3.8

The theory outlined above assumes that the sources S_1 and S_2 are slits of negligible width, producing many equally bright fringes. Figure 3.7 shows that, although the fringes are equidistant, they are not equally bright. This is because the slits have a finite width.

The slit width is significant, because wavelets travelling to a point from different parts of the same slit do not have the same phase. This fact limits the number of bright fringes seen in the pattern. Wider slits give fewer fringes, and not all fringes are equally bright. You are, in fact, observing a double slit diffraction pattern (you will learn more about this in the unit *Vibrations and waves*). In the following questions you can assume that the slits have negligible width.

Q **3.14 Self-assessment question**
In a Young's slit experiment the slits are 5.0×10^{-4} m apart and the distance between the slits and the screen is 2.0 m. The experiment is performed using a white light source, first with a filter which passes only blue light ($\lambda = 4.5 \times 10^{-7}$ m) and then with a filter passing only yellow light ($\lambda = 6.0 \times 10^{-7}$ m).
(a) What is the fringe spacing in each case?
(b) Sketch graphs, on the same axes, showing how the light intensity varies with distance along the screen for blue light and for yellow light. Each graph should extend from the central maximum to the fourth bright fringe on one side of the centre.
(c) A filter which passes only blue light and yellow light, in equal intensities, is placed in front of the source. A black and white film is placed in the position of the screen. Using the data provided by your calculations and graphs, sketch a further graph to show how the blackening of the film will vary with distance from the centre of the pattern when the film is developed (assuming that blackening is proportional to the light intensity reaching the film).■

White light fringes

Young's original experiments were performed with white light. Let us analyse this kind of pattern by considering how the light intensity varies for particular colours of the spectrum.

Q **3.15 Development question***
(a) Sketch a graph (similar to figure 3.8) showing how the intensity will vary for blue light passing through a double slit, from the first minimum on one side to the third minimum on the other side of the centre.
(b) On the same diagram, sketch the intensity curve for red light passing through the same double slit. (Assume that $\lambda_{red}/\lambda_{blue} = 3/2$, and that the sources have the same intensity.)
(c) At which point on the screen is there always a maximum intensity for all colours? Explain this.
(d) Describe the appearance of the zero order bright fringe when a white light source is used.
(e) Describe the appearance of the first order bright fringe, saying how it differs from the central fringe.
(f) Will there be a minimum between the first and second bright fringes?
(g) Estimate the maximum number of fringes you are likely to observe with white light, and explain your estimate.■

AV **AV VW8 Slideset**
Diffraction patterns
This is mainly intended for use with the unit *Vibrations and waves*. However, it contains slides showing the patterns produced by double slits illuminated by monochromatic sources and by white light. Look at these slides and the accompanying notes to compare the intensity graphs you have drawn and the slides.

You can view white light fringes formed by two slits using the double slits prepared for experiment WP5. Hold the double slit close to your eye and view a distant line filament lamp. When Young's fringes are viewed with white light it is easy to locate the central (zero order) maximum, because the central fringe is different from the rest. This makes it easier to locate any movement in the fringe pattern.

Q 3.16 Self-assessment question
The arrangement in figure 3.9 produces white light fringes on a screen.
(a) What change in the pattern will be observed if the slit S is moved in the direction of the arrow?
(b) What will happen if, with S in its original position, the double slits are moved in the same direction?
(c) Will any changes in the brightness or spacing of the fringes be observed if slit S is moved towards the double slits? Can S be too near to the double slits? Suggest reasons, remembering that S_1 and S_2 are illuminated by light diffracted through S.■

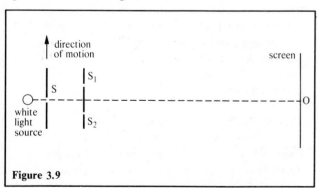

Figure 3.9

SYLLABUS EXTENSION

Fresnel's biprism

Figure 3.10 shows how an interference pattern can be produced using a single slit S and a biprism placed with its refracting edges parallel to the slit S. Light is refracted through the two halves of the biprism so that it appears to come from two virtual images S_1 and S_2 which are coherent sources. The fringe separation is $\lambda d/D$, as for Young's fringes, but notice that D is the distance from the screen to the slit S because the image slits S_1 and S_2 are also located in this plane.

A glass prism of very small angle A deviates light by an angle $(n - 1)A$ where n is the refractive index of the glass.

Q 3.17 Development question*
(a) Write down an equation relating angles A and θ.
(b) What factors determine the value of slit separation d?
(c) If A is a small angle, write down an equation for d in terms of A and other quantities. In what units must A be expressed?
(d) Calculate the value of d if $n = 1.50$, $A = 8.7 \times 10^{-3}$ rad and $l = 10$ cm.
(e) If the screen is placed 90 cm beyond the prism, what is the separation between the fringes if the wavelength of the source is 500 nm? $(1 \, nm = 10^{-9} \, m)$
(f) To change the separation of the fringes you can move the screen or, with the screen a fixed distance from the source, you can move the prism. Explain how you would double the fringe separation by each method (separately).■

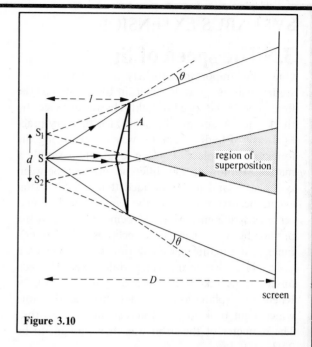

Figure 3.10

Fresnel's biprism can be used to measure the wavelength of a source experimentally, but in this case A and n are unknown and the separation d of the slits is found by using a converging lens.

Q 3.18 Study question
(a) Explain how the wavelength of the light from a monochromatic source can be determined experimentally using a Fresnel biprism.
(b) Explain why the fringe pattern observed using a biprism is brighter than the pattern produced by Young's double slits.■

3.5 The speed of light

One other important property of light which was studied was its speed. Roemer, in 1675, obtained the first value of the speed of light. He was engaged, by the French Academy of Science, for the very practical task of finding a better way of measuring the longitude of a place. Finding longitude is simply a matter of knowing the difference in time between two places, and it was decided that some celestial event, occurring daily at the same instant, could serve as a reference timing. Roemer found that the period between successive eclipses of Jupiter's innermost satellite varied during the course of a year. The maximum time difference, between observations taken six months apart, was 1320 s. Roemer's explanation was that this was the time which light took to travel across the earth's orbit. The diameter of the orbit was then thought to be 2.93×10^8 km.

Q 3.19 Self-assessment question

(a) What value would Roemer's results give for the speed of light?

(b) Modern timing methods give a maximum time lag of 16 minutes 36 seconds. This represents the time for light to travel across an orbit of diameter 2.98×10^8 km. What value of c is obtained from these results? ■

People have been devising methods of measuring the speed of light throughout the last 300 years. Measurement of the speed of light in different media was needed to test between Huygens' and Newton's explanations of refraction. This was obtained, in 1860, by Foucault.

As the nature of light became better understood, the importance of its speed in vacuum became more obvious. It was realised that this speed c was one of the most important constants in the universe. It was the speed, not just of light, but of all electromagnetic waves in vacuum. The constant c^2 was found to relate mass and energy in the special theory of relativity.

Because light travels at such a high speed, the time intervals to be measured are very small, even when the light is timed over large distances. Early methods measured its speed over astronomical distances. As timing methods were improved, the distance of travel was reduced to the order of a metre.

Two main terrestrial methods have been used:
1 'Chopped' light beam methods: measuring the transit time for short light pulses between leaving and returning through a gate, such as the gap in a toothed wheel (Fizeau's method, 1899) or an electric shutter (Anderson's method using a Kerr cell, 1941).
2 Rotating mirror methods: measuring transit time by reflecting light from a rotating mirror at the beginning and end of its measured path.

Q 3.20 Study question

Describe, with a diagram, one terrestrial method of measuring the speed of light, explaining which quantities are measured, and how a relationship is derived for the velocity of light. Give a set of typical values for the various quantities which appear in the relationship. ■

Q 3.21 Self-assessment question

The distance from the earth to the moon has been measured by sending out a short burst of laser light from the earth and receiving back the light after it has been reflected from a reflector placed on the moon by astronauts.

(a) The laser pulse from the earth lasts 10 ns. How long (in metres) is the wavetrain sent out in this time, if the speed of light is 3.0×10^8 m s^{-1}?

(b) The time taken by the pulse to travel there and back was measured to an accuracy of ± 10 ns. What uncertainty (in metres) in the calculated value of the moon's distance does this timing method produce?

(c) An error may arise in the calculated distance if the effect of the earth's atmosphere is ignored. The refractive index of the earth's atmosphere at sea level is 1.0003, and the entire atmosphere is equivalent to an atmosphere 8 km high compressed to the density it has at sea level. What error, in metres, will be involved if the change of speed of light in the atmosphere is ignored? Would the calculated distance be too large or too small? Would this matter if you were using the timing method described in (b)? ■

The internationally accepted value of c is
299 792 459.0 $\pm$ 0.8 m s^{-1}.

(The APPIL *Student's Handbook* introduces the estimation of experimental errors with data on the speed of light.)

Questions on objectives

1 State Snell's law and define the absolute refractive index of a medium. Use Huygens' construction to construct a refracted plane wavefront and show how this explanation is related to the above definitions.

(objective 6)

2 A circular ripple (figure 3.11) originates at point O then travels at 21 cm s^{-1} to a boundary where the depth of water changes. After refraction the ripples appear to originate from a point I located 15 cm from the boundary. Construct wavefronts to enable you to find the wave speed where the depth is b. On which side of the boundary is the depth greatest?

(objective 6)

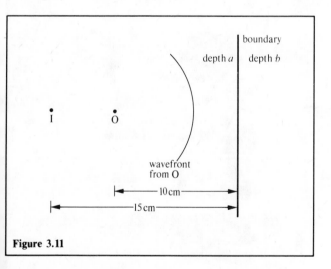

Figure 3.11

3 Explain the statement 'Glass is a dispersive medium for light'.

(objective 3)

4 Describe, giving the necessary theory, how the wavelength of monochromatic light can be found using Young's slits. Explain briefly how the conditions necessary to produce a stationary interference pattern are satisfied in the experiment.

(objectives 2, 4, 5)

5 Figure 3.12 shows an arrangement for obtaining Young's fringes. When a monochromatic source of green light is used, the fringe separation is 1.0 mm. Describe briefly what you will see on the screen in the following cases.

(a) The slit separation is reduced to $d/2$.

(b) The distance D is increased to $3D/2$, with the original slit separation.

(c) The slit separation is unchanged, but one slit is made twice as wide as the other.

(d) The original slit arrangement is used, but with a white light source.

(e) With the white light source, a red filter is placed in front of the slits.

(f) With a white light source, the primary slit S is moved slowly in the direction shown by the arrow.

(objectives 5, 7)

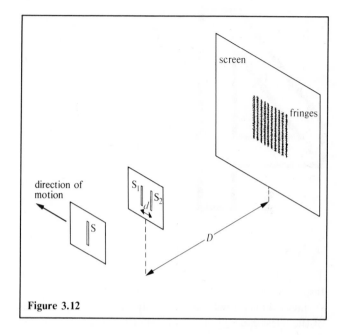

Figure 3.12

Chapter

Using light

Aim

This chapter revises and extends your previous studies on the reflection and refraction of light, at plane and curved surfaces. This knowledge is then applied to the principles of the telescope and other optical instruments.

References

Duncan MM   Chapter 5
Nelkon   Chapters 17 to 23
Whelan   Chapters 31 to 36

Experiments in chapter 4

WP6   Refractive index by apparent depth
($\frac{3}{4}$ hour)
WP7   Refractive index by critical angle
(1 hour)
WP8   The converging lens
(1 hour)
WP9   The astronomical telescope
($\frac{3}{4}$ hour)

Chapter 4

Study time: 2 weeks

Objectives

When you have completed the work in this chapter you should be able to:

1   Use the following scientific terms correctly: critical angle, total internal reflection, apparent depth, minimum deviation, refracting angle of a prism, focal plane, virtual object, entrance pupil, exit pupil, normal adjustment, power of a lens, eye-ring, near point, least distance of distinct vision.

2   Define the following scientific terms: refractive index, principal axis, optical centre, principal focus, focal length, linear magnification, angular magnification.

3   Explain what is meant by total internal reflection and critical angle and give practical applications of each.

4   State the laws of refraction.

5   Recall and use the relationship between refractive index, real depth and apparent depth (for normal incidence).

6   Recall and use the relationship between the refractive index of the material of a prism, the refracting angle and the angle of minimum deviation.

7   State the significance of a sign convention and use the 'real is positive' sign convention correctly in calculations.

8   Describe and explain experiments to determine the focal lengths of thin lenses.

9   Derive and use an expression for the equivalent focal length of two or more thin lenses in contact.

10   Describe the optical system and action of a refracting astronomical telescope in normal adjustment, including diagrams of the paths of rays of light through the telescope from a distant non-axial point.

11   Derive and recall an expression for the angular magnification of a refracting astronomical telescope in normal adjustment.

12   Describe the construction of a spectrometer, and explain how it is adjusted and used to determine the refractive index of the material of a prism.

13   Solve problems involving refractive index, refraction through prisms and thin lenses, and the angular magnification of an optical instrument.

14   EXTENSION
Describe and explain experiments to measure the refractive index of solids and liquids, including real and apparent depth and critical angle methods.

15   EXTENSION
Derive an expression for the refractive index of the material of a prism in terms of the refracting angle and the angle of minimum deviation.

16   EXTENSION
Recall and use the full lens formula relating the focal length, refractive index and radii of curvature of the surfaces of the lens.

17   EXTENSION
Describe and explain experiments to determine the focal length of spherical mirrors.

18   EXTENSION
Solve problems involving the use of
(a) the mirror formula,
(b) the full lens formula.

19   EXTENSION
Describe the optical system and action of a compound microscope, and draw diagrams of the paths of rays from a non-axial point which produce an image
(a) at the near point,
(b) at infinity.

20   EXTENSION
(a) Explain the function of the main components of a camera.
(b) Explain the significance of the *f*-number and the meaning of depth of field.

4.1 The ray concept

In the previous chapter you studied the wave nature of light and found that the wavelength is very small (less than a millionth of a metre). Because of this, diffraction effects due to light waves occur on a very small scale and are difficult to observe, except in a few cases when the light waves are restricted by tiny apertures. This is why our common experience persuades us that light is not diffracted round corners but travels in straight lines.

In this chapter we shall *not* consider waves restricted by tiny apertures or obstacles and so we shall ignore diffraction effects and consider the behaviour of light in terms of *rays*. We have already (in chapter 2) defined a ray as a normal to the wavefront, and also as a line which indicates the direction in which the wave energy is travelling.

You may have studied the behaviour of light by observing very narrow beams or 'ray streaks'. We can observe beams when they strike a reflecting surface or when light in the beam is scattered as it travels through dust or smoke particles. When a source produces a beam of light, the wave energy is concentrated within a limited cross-section. The path of the light energy – a ray – can be traced by observing the behaviour of very narrow beams. Even the narrowest beam, however, has a finite wavefront to which we can draw many normals. There is no such thing as a single ray. Nevertheless, the ray concept is very useful in describing the behaviour of light waves, just as lines (defined as having no thickness) are very useful in geometry even though we can never draw them. The behaviour of light waves, when they strike mirrors. lenses or prisms, is more conveniently described by rays than by wavefronts. *Geometrical optics* is the name given to the study of light in terms of rays. As this name implies, it is possible to describe much of what is observed in terms of simple geometry and a few basic laws.

Q **4.1 Self-assessment question**
(a) What is the meaning of the term *ray*?
(b) What is meant by a *converging beam*? Use the words wave or wavefront in your answer.
(c) Explain why you can draw two rays crossing each other without affecting each other.■

4.2 Refraction at plane surfaces

When light travels from one medium to another (for example, from air to glass) part of it is reflected back into the first medium and the rest of it travels in the second medium in a different direction.

Q **4.2 Study question**
State the laws which apply to the reflection and the refraction illustrated in figure 4.1.■

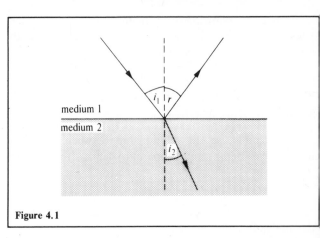

Figure 4.1

Q **4.3 Self-assessment question**
Why is it necessary to define absolute refractive index for a specific colour of light?■

4.4 Study question

When a ray passes from vacuum (or air) through two or more media with parallel boundaries, it will emerge in the vacuum (or air) laterally displaced but parallel to the original incident direction. Show that in this case, for each medium,

➤ $n \sin i = \text{constant}$,

where n is the absolute refractive index and i the angle of incidence for a particular medium.■

4.5 Self-assessment question

(a) Will a ray of light be refracted towards or away from the normal when travelling from glass to water? Explain. (Refractive index of water = 1.33, refractive index of glass = 1.50.)

(b) A ray of light travelling in glass strikes a plane glass – water interface at an angle of incidence of 50°. Calculate the angle of refraction in the water.■

Real and apparent depth

A pool of water appears to be less deep than it really is, when viewed from above the surface, because rays of light from a point O (figure 4.2a) are refracted away from the normal at the water – air interface and appear to come from point I. This is the image position for normal viewing. In figure 4.2b the same object O, viewed obliquely, will appear to be at I_1. As the viewing position becomes more oblique, the image moves along the path shown, getting nearer to the surface.

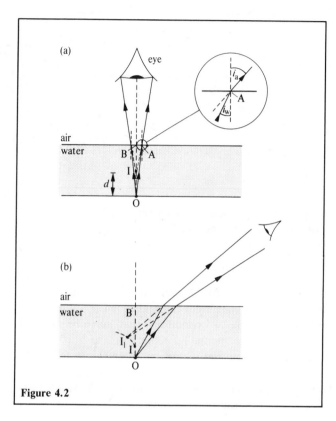

Figure 4.2

4.6 Development question

In figure 4.2a, for refraction at point A from water to air,

$$n_w \sin i_w = n_a \sin i_a,$$

where n_w and n_a are the absolute refractive indices for water and air respectively.

(a) Show that for normal viewing, when i_w and i_a are both small angles,

$$\frac{\sin i_a}{\sin i_w} = \frac{OB}{IB} = n_w.$$

(b) The distance OI is called the displacement, d, of the object. If the real depth is t, show that

$$d = t(1 - 1/n_w).■$$

4.7 Self-assessment question

A travelling microscope is focused on a scratch on the bottom of a beaker. Turpentine is poured into the beaker to a depth of 4.00 cm, and the microscope is raised through a vertical distance of 1.30 cm to bring the scratch into focus again. Calculate the refractive index of turpentine.■

EXTENSION

4.8 Study question

Explain why the position of the image (figure 4.2b) changes as the observer moves sideways and the angle i_a increases. Use the terms caustic curve and cusp in your answer.■

Total internal reflection and critical angle

If a ray of light is travelling from one medium to an optically less dense medium (for example, from glass to air) with an angle of incidence of about 30°, it is refracted away from the normal. Part of the incident light is also reflected.

Q **4.9 Self-assessment question**
(a) What happens to the angle of refraction as the angle of incidence is gradually increased?
(b) What is the maximum value of the angle of refraction?■

The name given to the limiting value of the angle of incidence, for which the refracted ray just emerges along the boundary between the two media, is the *critical angle*, c (figure 4.3). If the angle of incidence is increased beyond the critical angle, the reflected ray becomes suddenly brighter and no refracted ray is observed. All the incident light is being reflected, and *total internal reflection* occurs.

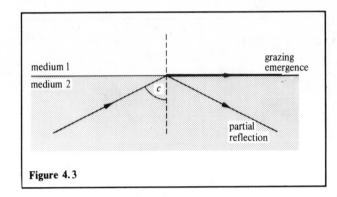

Figure 4.3

Q **4.10 Self-assessment question**
(a) By applying Snell's law to the critical ray, show that

$$n_2/n_1 = 1/\sin c.$$

(b) Calculate the critical angle for an air – glass boundary, if the refractive index of the glass is 1.50.
(c) What are the two conditions that must be satisfied in order for total internal reflection to occur?
(d) What do you find if you try to calculate the angle of refraction for an angle of incidence greater than the critical angle? How does the mathematical result correspond to physical observation?■

Q **4.11 Study question**
Explain, with the aid of diagrams, how a right-angled isosceles prism can be used to deviate a ray of light through (i) 90° and (ii) 180°.■

Q **4.12 Self-assessment question**
In figure 4.4, ABCD is a plan view of a glass cube. A horizontal beam of light enters the face AB at grazing incidence.
(a) Show that the emergent angle θ for rays emerging from AD is given by $\sin \theta = 1/\tan c$, where c is the critical angle.
(b) What is the greatest value that the refractive index of the glass may have if any of the light is to emerge from AD?
(c) If the glass has a greater refractive index than this, where will the light emerge?■

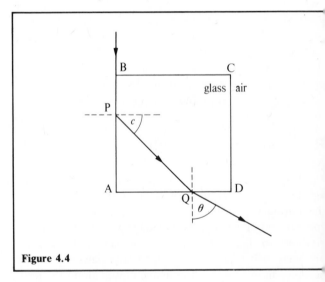

Figure 4.4

Because of the phenomenon of total internal reflection, it is possible to 'pipe' light along a bent transparent rod, provided that the curvature of the rod is not too great. A beam of light entering one end of the rod is totally internally reflected when it meets a wall, and is trapped within the rod, eventually emerging from the other end with little loss of intensity. Very thin transparent fibres behave in the same way, and the study of their properties and applications is an active field of research and development known as fibre optics. Devices using bundles of optical fibres have a wide range of applications. In medical science, for example, light pipes can be used for examining the interior of the lungs. In telecommunications, they can be used for the transmission of pulses of light which can carry large quantities of information.

4.3 Measurement of refractive index

E **Experiment WP 6**
Refractive index by apparent depth
In this experiment you will use a travelling microscope to measure the refractive index of glass.

The measurement of critical angle is one of the more important methods for determining refractive index. There are several ways of measuring this angle. The air-cell method is suitable for liquids if a large quantity of liquid is available.

Two thin parallel plates, separated by a layer of air, form the air-cell, which can be rotated about a vertical axis. This is immersed vertically in a rectangular trough of liquid. Figure 4.5 shows a plan view of the arrangement.

Q **4.13 Study question**
(a) Using figure 4.5, show that $n_1 = 1/\sin i_1$, where n_1 is the refractive index of the liquid.
(b) Make brief notes on an experimental method of measuring the refractive index of a liquid using this formula. Explain which angles are measured and why a monochromatic source of light is desirable. ∎

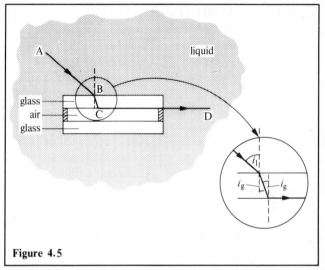

Figure 4.5

E **Experiment WP 7**
Refractive index by critical angle
The aim of this experiment is to measure the refractive index of a small quantity of liquid.

4.4 Refraction by a prism

Prisms are used in optical instruments to produce deviation (changes in direction) in the beams of light that pass through them. White light is separated into its constituent colours when it passes through a prism. This separation is often useful, as it provides a method whereby light from a source can be analysed. Sometimes it is a nuisance, as it may lead to coloured images. In this section we consider the deviation produced by a prism and the use of a spectrometer to measure refractive index (dispersion and spectra are studied in the unit *Vibrations and waves*).

Minimum deviation

The path of a ray of light through a prism can be traced by using a ray box or pins (figure 4.6a). When the light leaves the prism it does not travel in the same direction as it entered: it is *deviated*. The angle between the original direction of the light and the final direction is called the angle of deviation, *D*.

Figure 4.6b shows the results of an experiment to investigate the relationship between the angle of incidence and the angle of deviation.

Q **4.14 Self-assessment question**
(a) What happens to the angle of deviation as the angle of incidence is increased from a small value?
(b) Why are there no values of *D* for small angles of incidence?■

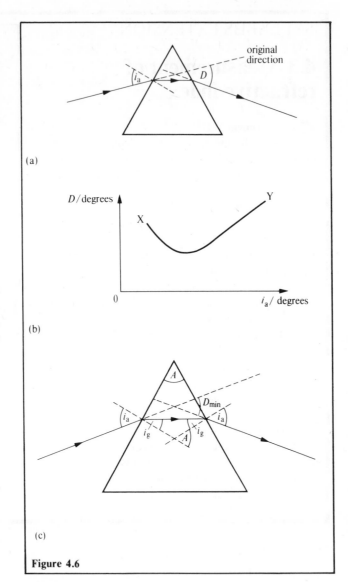

Figure 4.6

It can be demonstrated experimentally, and proved theoretically, that the deviation is a minimum when the light passes symmetrically through the prism, as shown in figure 4.6c (the face opposite A plays no part). The angle D_{min} is called the angle of minimum deviation. It is related to the refracting angle A of the prism and its refractive index n_g by the equation

$$n_g = \frac{\sin \frac{1}{2}(A + D_{min})}{\sin \frac{1}{2}A}.$$

Q **4.15 Self-assessment question**
The above formula is valid only for a prism whose refracting angle A is less than twice the critical angle. Explain why.■

SYLLABUS EXTENSION

Q **4.16 Study question**
Derive the relationship between the refractive index of the material of a prism, its refracting angle and the angle of minimum deviation.■

Q **4.17 Self-assessment question**
A 60° prism is made of glass with a refractive index, for yellow light, of 1.60.
(a) What is the angle of incidence at which minimum deviation occurs?
(b) What is the angle of minimum deviation?■

The spectrometer

Figure 4.7 shows the main components of the instrument. Light from the collimator passes through the prism, and the resulting spectrum can be examined through the telescope. The spectrometer is fitted with an angular scale so that the angle between the collimator and telescope can be measured, and we shall be concerned here with its use in an accurate method for measuring the refractive index of glass for a particular wavelength of light. (The use of the spectrometer for observing and measuring spectra is considered in the unit *Vibrations and waves*.)

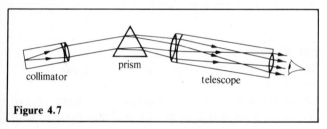

Figure 4.7

Q **4.18 Study question**
(a) Describe how you would adjust a spectrometer for use.
(b) Describe how you would use a spectrometer to measure the angle of a prism and the angle of minimum deviation. State what measurements you would take and how you would use them to find the refractive index of the material of the prism.■

If a spectrometer is available, set up and adjust the spectrometer for yourself and measure the refractive index of the glass of a prism for sodium light. (The same method can be used to measure the refractive index of a liquid. The liquid is enclosed in a hollow glass prism.)

Q **4.19 Self-assessment question**
A prism whose refracting angle is 60° causes a minimum deviation of 46° in a monochromatic beam of light. Calculate the refractive index of the prism for that wavelength.■

4.5 Thin lenses

There are many different shapes of lens, but all lenses can be classified as either converging or diverging. We shall restrict our study to thin lenses, for which the diameter of the lens is large compared to its maximum thickness.

Q **4.20 Study question**
Define the following terms as applied to a converging lens and a diverging lens: principal axis, optical centre C, principal focus F, focal length *f*, and focal plane.■

Lens calculations

Information about the position and nature of the image formed by a lens can be obtained either by drawing a ray diagram or by calculation. Both methods are shown in the worked example in figure 4.8, which also summarises the 'real is positive' sign convention and some lens formulae. In lens calculations using these formulae, only small objects on the principal axis are considered. All rays are therefore *paraxial* (close to the principal axis and making small angles with it).

'Real is positive' sign convention

POSITIVE
Distances actually traversed by rays, i.e. distances between *real* objects or images and the optical centre of a lens or mirror.

Focal length of *converging* lens.

Radius of curvature of lens surface if *convex* to the less dense medium.

Focal length and radius of curvature of a *concave* mirror.

NEGATIVE
Distances apparently traversed by rays, i.e. distances between *virtual* objects or images and the optical centre of a lens or mirror.

Focal length of *diverging* lens.

Radius of curvature of lens surface if *concave* to the less dense medium.

Focal length and radius of curvature of a *convex* mirror.

Lens formula

$$\frac{1}{f} = \frac{1}{u} + \frac{1}{v}$$

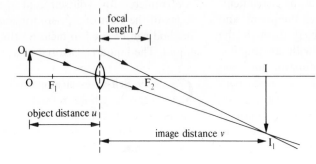

Linear magnification m

$$m = \frac{\text{image height (or width)}}{\text{object height (or width)}}$$

$$m = \frac{II_1}{OO_1} = \frac{v}{u}$$

Power of a lens

$$\text{power} = \frac{1}{\text{focal length}}$$

$$F = \frac{1}{f}$$

Worked example

Question

An object is placed 30 cm from a converging lens A of focal length 20 cm. Another converging lens B, of focal length 40 cm, is placed coaxially with A and 20 cm from it on the side away from the object. Find the position, nature and magnification of the image formed by the two lenses.

Calculation

For lens A, $f = +20$ cm, $u = +30$ cm.

$$\frac{1}{+20\,\text{cm}} = \frac{1}{+30\,\text{cm}} + \frac{1}{v}$$
$$\frac{1}{v} = \frac{1}{+20\,\text{cm}} - \frac{1}{+30\,\text{cm}}$$
$$\frac{1}{v} = \frac{1}{+60\,\text{cm}}$$
$$v = +60\,\text{cm}$$

Magnification produced by lens A = 60/30 = 2.

Figure 4·8

The light is intercepted by lens B 20 cm from lens A. The image formed by lens A acts as a virtual object for lens B.

For lens B, $f = +40$ cm, $u = -40$ cm.

$$\frac{1}{+40\,\text{cm}} = \frac{1}{-40\,\text{cm}} + \frac{1}{v}$$
$$\frac{1}{v} = \frac{1}{+40\,\text{cm}} - \frac{1}{-40\,\text{cm}}$$
$$\frac{1}{v} = \frac{2}{+40\,\text{cm}}$$
$$v = +20\,\text{cm}$$

Magnification produced by lens B = 20/40 = $\frac{1}{2}$.
Total magnification = $2 \times \frac{1}{2} = 1$.
The final image is 20 cm from B, on the side away from A, real, and the same size as the object.

Ray diagram

Real rays are shown by solid lines, virtual rays by broken lines.

Lenses or mirrors are represented by straight broken lines, with a small lens or mirror drawn in the middle to indicate the type used.

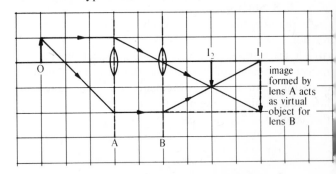

image formed by lens A acts as virtual object for lens B

Q 4.21 Study question

A lens can be regarded as being made up of a large number of thin prisms. Deduce, by this method, an expression for the focal length of a lens in terms of the object distance and the image distance. ■

Q 4.22 Self-assessment question

(a) A converging lens of focal length 15 cm forms a virtual image 20 cm from the lens. What values would you substitute in the lens formula to calculate the object distance?

(b) An object is placed 10 cm from a diverging lens of focal length 20 cm. What values would you substitute in the lens formula to calculate the image distance? ■

Q 4.23 Self-assessment question

(a) An object is placed 10 cm from a converging lens of focal length 20 cm. Calculate the position, nature and magnification of the image.

(b) What is the nature of the image formed by a diverging lens of a real object? Sketch a ray diagram to show how it is formed.

(c) An erect image, 2 cm high, is formed 10 cm from a diverging lens of focal length 15 cm. Calculate the position and size of the object. ■

Q 4.24 Self-assessment question

Two thin lenses are placed coaxially 15 cm apart. A beam of light parallel to the axis strikes the first lens, which is a converging lens of focal length 20 cm. The second lens is a diverging lens, also of focal length 20 cm.

(a) Sketch the paths of two rays of light through the optical system and show the position of the final image.

(b) Calculate the position of the final image using the lens formula. Is it a real or a virtual image? ■

Two thin lenses in contact

Q 4.25 Development question

When two thin lenses A and B, of focal lengths f_1 and f_2, are placed in contact, the combination acts as a single thin lens. Figure 4.9 shows two converging lenses in contact.

(a) If lens B was not present, lens A would form a real image of an object at O at I_1. Write an expression for f_1 in terms of u and x.

(b) When lens B is in position, I_1 acts as a virtual object for lens B and a real image is formed at I. Write an expression for f_2 in terms of v and x. (Make sure you have the correct sign for the object distance.)

(c) Using the expressions derived in (a) and (b), show that

$$\frac{1}{f} = \frac{1}{f_1} + \frac{1}{f_2}$$

where f is the equivalent focal length of the combination.

(d) Show that, if a converging lens of focal length 20 cm is in contact with a diverging lens of focal length 30 cm, the result is a converging combination of focal length 60 cm. ■

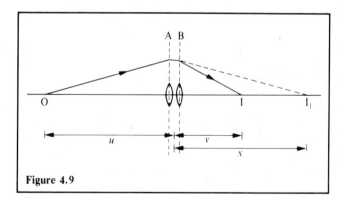

Figure 4.9

The focal length of a lens depends on the refractive index of the material of the lens. For glass, $n_{red} > n_{blue}$. This produces an effect called *chromatic aberration*.

Q 4.26 Self-assessment question
(a) Sketch the paths of the refracted red and blue rays produced when a parallel beam of white light passes through a converging lens.
(b) Describe what you would see on a screen, perpendicular to the axis, which was moved slowly along the axis towards the lens through the region in which the beam is focused. ■

Q 4.27 Study question
Explain briefly how chromatic aberration can be eliminated for two colours (and reduced for all) using an *achromatic doublet*. ■

Measuring focal length

A thin converging lens forms a real image of an object placed further away from the lens than the principal focus. The position of the image and its size (if necessary) can be found by experiment, and the focal length of the lens can be determined by a suitable graphical method. The following is a brief summary of the methods available for finding the focal length of a converging lens.
1 Measure u and v, and draw a graph of $1/u$ against $1/v$ or of u against v.
2 Place a plane mirror behind the lens and locate the point where the object and image coincide.
3 Measure m and v, and find f from the relationship $v/f = m + 1$.

Q 4.28 Self-assessment question
In an experiment a series of values of m and v are obtained.
(a) What values must be plotted to give a straight line graph?
(b) How may the focal length be obtained from the graph? ■

E Experiment WP8
The converging lens
In this experiment you will determine the focal length of a converging lens using an auxiliary plane mirror, and a graphical method.

A diverging lens cannot produce a real image if a diverging beam from a real object is incident at the lens. However, if the light from the object is made to converge sufficiently, by a converging lens, before it meets the diverging lens, a real image can be produced.

Q 4.29 Study question
Make brief notes on how you would determine the focal length of a diverging lens by using a converging lens (i) of shorter focal length, and (ii) of longer focal length, than the diverging lens. Draw ray diagrams to illustrate the methods used, and show how the results are calculated. ■

Depth of field

While the main use of the stop is to control the intensity of light which passes through the lens, it has a second important use. It controls the depth of field. This is the distance between the positions of an object at which its image is acceptably in focus. Figure 4.10 shows that a large aperture ($f/4$, with a 200 mm lens) has a small depth of field: the subject stands out against a fuzzy background. A smaller aperture ($f/32$) has a much larger depth of field: the background detail can be seen quite clearly.

Q **4.32 Study question**
Explain with the aid of a ray diagram why reducing the aperture increases the depth of field.■

Figure 4.10

SYLLABUS EXTENSION

Wavefronts through lenses

When a spherical wavefront from a point object is incident at a thin spherical lens, it is refracted to produce a spherical wavefront converging to a real image, or diverging from a virtual image.

Q **4.33 Study question**
Sketch the wavefronts from a point object on the axis of a converging lens, showing how the light waves may be refracted to produce a virtual image.■

The full lens formula

Q **4.34 Development question***
In figure 4.11a, PQRS represents a biconvex lens whose material has an absolute refractive index n. The radius of curvature of the surface PQR is r_1, and that of surface PSR is r_2. EQF is a spherical wavefront from a point object O, which after refraction becomes wavefront GSH, converging to a point image I.

(a) Justify the expression EG = nQS.
(b) Figure 4.11b illustrates a property of intersecting chords of a circle, applied to the wavefront EQF to obtain an expression for JQ in terms of x and the appropriate radius. Obtain similar expressions for QC, CS and SK.

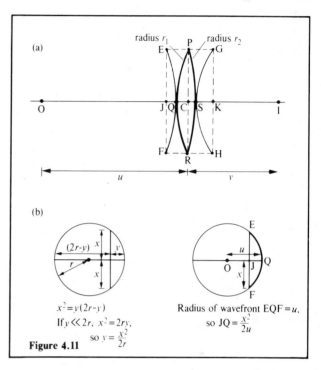

$x^2 = y(2r-y)$
If $y \ll 2r$, $x^2 = 2ry$,
so $y = \frac{x^2}{2r}$

Radius of wavefront EQF = u,
so JQ = $\frac{x^2}{2u}$

Figure 4.11

(c) The expression in part (a) can be rewritten as

$$JQ + QC + CS + SK = n(QC + QS).$$

Use this equation and the expressions derived in part (b) to show that

$$\frac{1}{u} + \frac{1}{v} = (n-1)\left(\frac{1}{r_1} + \frac{1}{r_2}\right).■$$

When $u = \infty$, $v = f$, hence

$$\rightarrow \quad \frac{1}{f} = (n-1)\left(\frac{1}{r_1} + \frac{1}{r_2}\right).$$

This relationship is sometimes called the 'lens-maker's formula'. In order to make this expression cover all cases, the radius of curvature is given a positive sign if the surface is convex to the less dense medium, and a negative sign if the surface is concave to the less dense medium.

Q **4.35 Self-assessment question**
Four lenses of different shapes are made of glass with a refractive index of 1.5. Each is bounded by surfaces whose radii of curvature are 20 cm and 30 cm. The shapes of the lenses are (i) biconvex, (ii) concavo-convex (converging meniscus), (iii) biconcave, (iv) convex-concave (diverging meniscus). Calculate the focal length of each lens.■

Q **4.36 Self-assessment question**
A thin equiconvex lens is made of glass of refractive index 1.6. When an object is placed 10 cm from the lens, a virtual image five times the size of the object is formed.
(a) Calculate the focal length of the lens.
(b) Calculate the radii of curvature of the lens surfaces.■

Q **4.37 Study question**
Make brief notes on each of the following. Illustrate your answers with ray diagrams and explain how the results are obtained from the measurements.
(a) Explain how you would determine the radius of curvature of the surfaces of a converging lens, using an optical method (e.g., Boys' method).
(b) Explain how you would use a converging lens and a plane mirror to find the refractive index of a small quantity of liquid.■

Q **4.38 Self-assessment question**
An equiconvex lens made of glass with refractive index 1.6 rests on a horizontal plane mirror. An object is coincident with its own image when it is 1.0 m above the lens. When liquid is placed between the lens and the mirror the object has to be raised 0.75 m for coincidence to occur again. Calculate the refractive index of the liquid. (Hint: first find the radius of curvature of the lens surface.)■

4.6 Spherical mirrors

Spherical mirrors reflect light so that a parallel beam can be made convergent (by a concave mirror) or divergent (by a convex mirror). A concave mirror can perform a similar task to a converging lens. For example, telescopes can be constructed using either a converging lens or a concave mirror. This brief study of the optical properties of mirrors is confined mainly to mirrors of small aperture, that is, mirrors for which the diameter (distance across) is small compared to the radius of curvature. When large aperture mirrors are required (for example, for headlamp reflectors) they are usually made parabolic, not spherical, because a large aperture spherical mirror has no precise focus and does not produce clear images.

Q **4.39 Study question**
Define the focal length of a spherical mirror, using and explaining the terms 'paraxial rays' and 'principal focus'.■

Q **4.40 Study question**
Show that for a spherical mirror the focal length approximately equal to half its radius of curvature indicating the approximations which are applicable.■

Mirror calculations

For paraxial rays incident at a spherical mirror of small aperture,

$$\frac{2}{r} = \frac{1}{f} = \frac{1}{u} + \frac{1}{v}$$

where r is the radius of curvature, u the object distance and v the image distance. This formula is applicable to all spherical mirrors for objects at any distance from the mirror, provided the sign convention ('real is positive') is applied. On this convention the focal length of a concave mirror is positive.

Q 4.41 Study question
By applying the laws of reflection to a concave mirror forming a real image, show that

$$\frac{1}{f} = \frac{1}{u} + \frac{1}{v}. \ \blacksquare$$

Q 4.42 Study question
Draw a ray diagram to show how a convex mirror forms a virtual, erect, diminished image. ■

Q 4.43 Self-assessment question
A concave mirror forms an erect image 45 cm from the object and four times its height.
(a) Where must the mirror be situated?
(b) What is its radius of curvature?
(c) Through what distance must the object be moved to form an inverted image of the same magnification? ■

Measurement of focal length

The focal length of a concave mirror can be found by (i) adjusting the position of an object until it coincides with its own image, or (ii) obtaining several values for object and image distances and finding f from a graph of $1/u$ against $1/v$.

Q 4.44 Study question
Make brief notes on the above methods of measuring the focal length of a concave mirror. ■

The focal length of a convex mirror can be found by using an auxiliary converging lens, as illustrated in figure 4.12. The position of the mirror is adjusted until the object coincides with its own image.

Q 4.45 Self-assessment question
(a) Explain why the centre of curvature of the mirror is also the position of the image formed by the lens in the absence of the mirror.
(b) What measurements would you take, and how would you find the radius of curvature of the mirror?
(c) Why is this a good method for making several independent measurements of r? ■

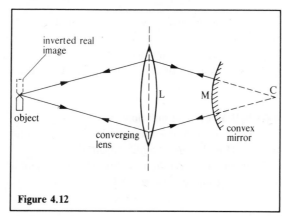

Figure 4.12

4.7 Optical instruments

An optical instrument is used to extend the limits of perception of the human eye. When an object is placed inside the principal focus of a converging lens, it forms a magnified image. This is a simple form of microscope. When we considered the magnification produced by a lens we introduced the idea of linear magnification m. In some optical instruments the final image is formed at infinity. In such a case m would be infinite! The linear magnification is therefore not a very helpful indication of the improvement produced by the optical instrument.

The apparent size of an object depends upon the size of its image formed on the retina of the eye. This depends upon the angle which is subtended at the eye (the visual angle). In figure 4.13 the image sizes of the two objects AB and CD will appear to be the same.

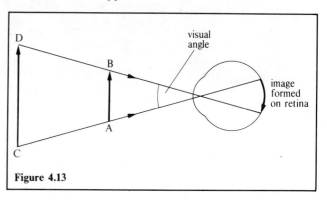

Figure 4.13

Q 4.46 Self-assessment question

Explain why the two cars shown in figure 4.14a appear to be the same size.■

Figure 4.14

The eye has the ability to *accommodate* (i.e. to change the converging power of the lens system), so that it can see clearly objects situated over a wide, but limited, range of distances. The rays emerging from an optical instrument must therefore appear to come from an image in this region of clear vision.

Q 4.47 Study question

What is meant by the terms accommodation, near point, far point and least distance of distinct vision?■

Angular magnification

Telescopes and microscopes are instruments designed to produce an image which subtends a greater angle at the eye than the original object does. They make objects look bigger by producing a bigger image on the retina of the eye.

The angular magnification M (or magnifying power) of an optical instrument is defined by the equation

$$M = \frac{\beta}{a}$$

where β is the angle subtended at the eye by the final image formed by the instrument, and a is the angle subtended at the eye by the object, at some specified distance, without the use of the instrument.

Telescopes view distant fixed objects, so for telescopes a is the angle subtended at the unaided eye by the fixed distant object.

When examining small objects with the unaided eye, the best we can do is bring them as close as possible to the eye, to the near point. So for microscopes the angle a is the angle subtended by the object when placed at the least distance of distinct vision.

Q 4.48 Self-assessment question

(a) What is the distinction between angular magnification M and linear magnification m?
(b) Write down an equation defining the angular magnification of a microscope.■

Magnifying glass

Q 4.49 Study question

(a) Describe, with the aid of a ray diagram, how a converging lens can be used as a magnifying glass so that the final image is at the near point (i.e. the instrument is in normal adjustment).
(b) Where must the object be placed so that the final image is at infinity?■

Q 4.50 Development question

An expression for the angular magnification M of a magnifying glass can be derived in terms of the focal length f and the least distance of distinct vision D. Figure 4.15 shows a magnifying glass producing an image at the near point, viewed by an eye very close to the lens.
(a) Calculate the object distance u in terms of f and D.
(b) Hence show that the angular magnification M is given by

$$M = (D/f) + 1$$

(assuming angles a and β are small, so that $\tan \beta \approx \beta$, etc.).
(c) Show that when the final image is at infinity the magnifying power is given by $M = D/f$.■

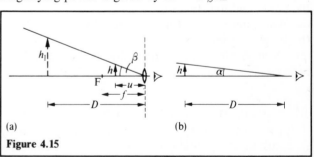

Figure 4.15

Q 4.51 Self-assessment question

(a) What is the focal length of the lens which can be used as a magnifying glass in normal adjustment with a magnifying power of 6?

(b) Using this lens, the image is located 300 mm from the eye. Calculate the object position and hence deduce the angular magnification produced in this case.

(c) Where must the final image be located to produce (i) maximum angular magnification and (ii) minimum angular magnification?■

Astronomical telescope

A refracting astronomical telescope is constructed using two converging lenses, a long focal length objective and a shorter focal length eyepiece (figure 4.16).

Q 4.52 Development question *

Figure 4.16 shows a beam of light which originated at one point; the top of a distant object. After passing through the telescope, the light is focused at a point on the retina of the observer's eye.

(a) What is located at the point between the lenses where the light converges? What is the distance from the objective lens to this point?

(b) What kind of image is the eye looking at, and where is it located?

(c) What kind of image is produced on the retina?

(d) What is the distance between the lenses of the telescope shown in figure 4.16?■

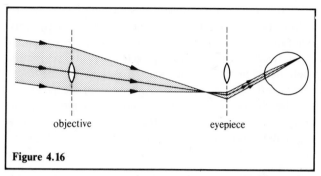

Figure 4.16

The telescope objective produces a real inverted image which acts as an object for the second lens. This is used as a simple magnifying glass, producing a virtual inverted image between the near and far points of the observer's eye. In normal adjustment the final image is located at infinity.

Figure 4.17 shows one ray from the top of a distant object, which passes through the optical centre of the objective and is refracted through the second lens. The position and size of image I_1, formed by the objective, is shown. How do we find the correct path for a ray from this image to the eye? If the final image is located at infinity, all the rays leaving the eyepiece will be parallel. The construction line through the centre of the eyepiece is one path which a ray could take through the lens without refraction, and if the image is at infinity all the rays emerging from the lens must be parallel to this construction line. We can use this diagram to find the magnifying power of the telescope.

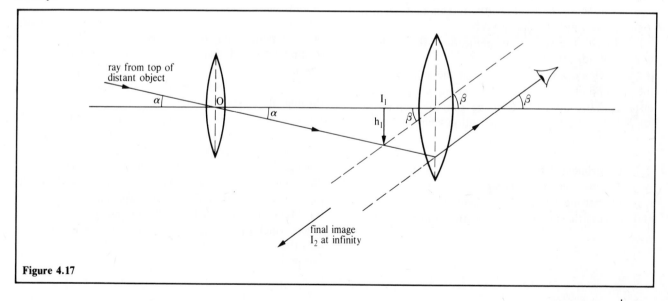

Figure 4.17

Q 4.53 Development question
(a) Why is the angle a (figure 4.17) the same as the angle subtended at the unaided eye by the object?
(b) Express a in terms of h_1 and f_o and β in terms of h_1 and f_e.
(c) Show that angular magnification $= f_o/f_e$, for normal adjustment.
(d) If the final image is not at a finite distance the magnification will be f_o/u, where u is the distance from the image I_1 to the eyepiece. Is the magnifying power greater or less than f_o/f_e in this case? Explain why.
(e) Suggest possible specifications for the lenses to be used in constructing a portable astronomical telescope of magnifying power 50. ■

Q 4.54 Self-assessment question
An astronomical telescope consists of two thin converging lenses of focal lengths 100 cm and 5 cm. It is used for viewing a distant object.
(a) Calculate the angular magnification when it is used in normal adjustment.
(b) The telescope is adjusted so that the final image is at the near point, 25 cm from the eyepiece. Calculate the distance of the intermediate image from the eyepiece.
(c) What is the angular magnification when it is used in near point adjustment? ■

E Experiment WP9
The astronomical telescope
In this experiment you will construct a simple telescope and measure the angular magnification it produces.

Now try drawing the paths of rays through a telescope to help to explain how it works. The purpose of such a ray diagram is not to locate exact image positions for particular lenses, but to show the general principle for all such instruments, so the exact positions of the focal points will not be included. Any appropriate positions can be chosen for the object and the images but the images must be drawn to the correct sizes for their particular positions.

Q 4.55 Study question
Draw a ray diagram to show the paths of rays from two non-axial points (e.g. the top and bottom of an object) through an astronomical telescope in normal adjustment, following the instructions below.
(a) Draw a diagram like figure 4.17, showing the path of one ray accurately.
(b) Draw the paths of two more rays from the top of the object passing through the *top* and *bottom* of the objective (distinguish clearly between actual rays and construction lines).
(c) Suppose the object lies across the axis, with the axis through its midpoint. Draw three more rays, from the bottom of the object, making an angle a with the axis (first draw an image I_1 which has its midpoint on the axis).
(d) Shade the area between the extreme rays (i.e. rays through the top and bottom of the objective lens) from one point. (This indicates the region through which all rays must pass if they come from that point.)
(e) Mark the place where all possible rays from the object which pass through the telescope are concentrated into the smallest area (this area is called the *eye ring* or exit pupil). ■

The eye ring is the best position for the eye, since it is the place where most light can be received and where the observer has the widest field of view. In figure 4.18, the objective of a telescope is illuminated by light diffused by a ground glass screen. Rays from point A at the top of the objective lens converge to A_1 after passing through the eyepiece. A_1 is the real image of A; similarly, B_1 is the image of B. The eye ring or exit pupil is the image of the objective formed by the eyepiece.

Q 4.56 Study question
Show, by referring to figure 4.18, that for a telescope in normal adjustment the angular magnification M is given by

$$M = \frac{\text{diameter of objective}}{\text{diameter of eye ring}}.$$

Indicate briefly how you would check this result experimentally. ■

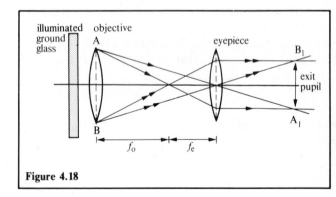

Figure 4.18

Q 4.57 Self-assessment question
(a) Why is it pointless to design a telescope with an exit pupil greater than about 2 mm (the diameter of the pupil of the eye)?
(b) An astronomical telescope is to be constructed from two converging lenses of focal lengths 96 cm and 4.0 cm. What will be the location of the eye ring?
(c) Suggest an appropriate diameter for the objective lens.■

In designing a telescope, the diameter of the objective must be related to the magnifying power, to produce the right size of eye ring. Large diameter objectives are desirable, because
1 the resolving power (the ability to separate close objects and observe fine detail) increases with the diameter of the objective (see the unit *Vibrations and waves*), and
2 a large objective collects more light.

Have you ever considered why a street lamp 50 m away looks just as bright as one 25 m away? Less light reaches your eye from the distant lamp, only a quarter as much as from the near lamp, because light spreads out from the source. But the visual angle for the distant lamp is half that for the near lamp. The image of the distant lamp on the retina is half as high and half as wide as that of the near lamp, so a quarter of the light is focused into a quarter of the area on the retina. The 'energy density' (light energy per unit area) is the same for both images, so the eye sees both street lamps as equally bright.

A telescope receives light through an objective lens and transmits it to the observer's eye. Think about the brightness of the images it produces.

Q 4.58 Study question
(a) Why does a telescope make point objects (stars) appear brighter? What factor determines how bright they appear?
(b) Explain why the image of the moon seen in a telescope can never appear brighter than the moon itself.■

Q 4.59 Study question
(a) What is an achromatic objective? Why is it desirable for a telescope to have one?
(b) Suggest why it is less important to have an achromatic eyepiece.■

SYLLABUS EXTENSION

Reflecting telescopes

A concave mirror, like a converging lens, forms a real image which can be magnified by an eyepiece. This is the principle of the reflecting telescope (figure 4.19). The mirror is ground and polished to a paraboloidal shape, so that a clear point image is produced of a distant point object (no spherical aberration).

A concave objective reflects light back into the path of the oncoming light, so it is necessary to deflect the rays going to the eyepiece so that the eyepiece can be placed in a convenient position. The Newtonian telescope uses a plane mirror to deflect the light to an eyepiece on the side of the telescope. The Cassegrain telescope uses a convex mirror to reflect the converging beam through a small hole in the centre of the concave objective.

Q 4.60 Study question
Make brief notes on one form of reflecting telescope. You should include a ray diagram, to illustrate its action, and discuss its advantages compared to a refracting telescope.■

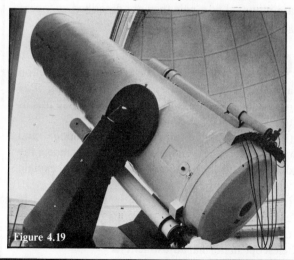
Figure 4.19

Telescopes for terrestrial use

A simple astronomical telescope can be modified for terrestrial use by arranging for the final image to be the right way up. This can be achieved by means of an 'erecting' lens, or by the use of totally internally reflecting prisms. For practical purposes the use of prisms is more convenient, as they make a small compact instrument. These telescopes are usually mounted in pairs and are known as prismatic binoculars.

Another form of terrestrial telescope was made by Galileo in 1609. He used a diverging lens instead of a converging lens as the eyepiece. This instrument does not produce a high magnification. When two are mounted as a pair they are described as 'opera glasses'.

Q 4.61 Study question
(a) Explain, with diagrams, the construction and optical action of prismatic binoculars. Pay particular attention to the orientation of the prisms to produce the correct inversions.
(b) Make brief notes on the construction and optical action of a Galilean telescope. Include a ray diagram with the final image at infinity, and explain why the eye ring is virtual.
(c) Explain how a converging lens can be used to convert an astronomical telescope into a terrestrial telescope. What is the minimum length of such a telescope in normal adjustment?■

The compound microscope

The magnifying glass is sometimes referred to as a simple microscope. A compound microscope obtains magnification in two stages. The objective is a converging lens of short focal length. If an object is placed just a little more than the focal length from the objective then an enlarged real image is produced. This image becomes the object for a second lens, the eyepiece, which acts as a simple magnifying glass. The final image produced by the eyepiece is located between the observer's near and far points. In normal adjustment the final image is located at the near point (since the microscope is normally used in conjunction with drawings or notes at this distance).

Figure 4.20 shows a ray from the top of an object passing through the optical centre of the objective and refracted at the eyepiece. An image I_1 is produced by the objective at a distance v from the eyepiece, and the image I_2 is produced by the eyepiece. The line through the centre of the eyepiece is a construction line, to enable image I_2 to be drawn to the correct size (a ray from the top of I_1 could travel along this line through the centre of the lens). In a microscope the distance between the objective and eyepiece is fixed and the microscope is focused by moving the whole microscope relative to the fixed object.

Q 4.62 Self-assessment question
If the microscope is used for prolonged observation, it is more restful for the eye to view a final image at infinity. How can the microscope shown in figure 4.20 be refocused to produce a final image at infinity? Explain your answer, stating how object and image distances change when the microscope tube is moved.■

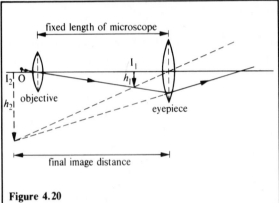

Figure 4.20

The angular magnification M for a microscope, simple or compound, is given by

$$M = \frac{\beta}{a}$$

where β is the visual angle for the final image produced by the microscope, and a is the visual angle when the object is at the near point.

Q 4.63 Development question

Use figure 4.20 and the above definition to show that angular magnification M = linear magnification produced by objective $\times$ linear magnification produced by eyepiece $\times$ D/v, where D is the least distance of distinct vision and v is the final image distance.■

As with telescopes, we can explain the principle of the microscope by drawing the paths of rays through the system. These diagrams are not construction diagrams, to locate image positions for particular lenses, but show the optical system for any microscope. Appropriate positions are chosen for the object and images and construction lines are used to determine their correct sizes for those locations.

Q 4.64 Study question

(a) Draw a diagram showing the paths through a microscope of three rays from the top of a small object which lies across the axis with its midpoint on the axis. The rays should pass through the centre, top and bottom of the objective.

(b) Draw three rays through the microscope from the bottom of the object.

(c) Locate the images formed, and distinguish clearly between construction lines and actual rays.

(d) Mark the eye ring.■

Q 4.65 Self-assessment question

A compound microscope has an objective lens, of focal length 40 mm, and an eyepiece, of focal length 60 mm, separated by 250 mm. An object 2.0 mm long is set up 50 mm from the objective lens.

(a) Calculate the position and size of the image formed by the objective lens.

(b) Calculate the position and size of the final image formed by the eyepiece.

(c) Calculate the angular magnification produced by the microscope.■

Questions on objectives

1 Figure 4.21 shows an optical dipstick. It consists of a perspex probe with a prismatic tip, with a lamp and a photocell mounted at the top. When the probe is in air, light from the lamp passes down the probe, is *totally internally reflected* twice at the prismatic end, returns up the probe and is reflected to the photocell. When the tip of the probe is immersed in a liquid, the *critical angle* is altered. Total internal reflection does not take place, and the beam no longer returns up the probe. The photocell therefore receives less light, its electrical resistance increases, and a signal is passed to the control box.

(a) Explain what is meant by total internal reflection and critical angle.

(b) Why does the critical angle change when the probe is immersed in a liquid (e.g. water) whose refractive index is less than that of perspex? Why does the beam no longer pass up the probe?

(c) Calculate the critical angle for the passage of light from perspex to air (the refractive index of perspex is 1.5).

(d) What happens to the light when the probe is immersed in a liquid whose refractive index is greater than that of perspex?

(objectives 1, 3, 13)

2 Explain what is meant by the angular magnification M of an astronomical telescope.

(objective 2)

3 Explain the essential features of a refracting astronomical telescope.

(objective 10)

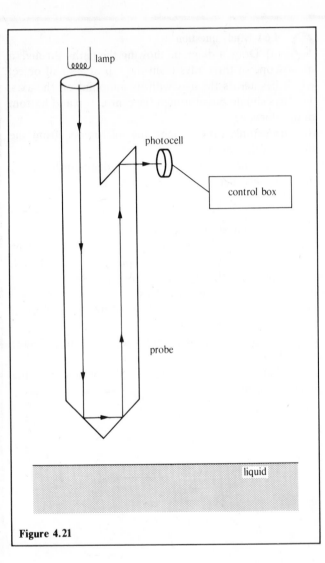

Figure 4.21

4 Which of the following expressions is the correct relationship for the angular magnification of an astronomical telescope in normal adjustment, where f_o and f_e are the focal lengths of the objective and eyepiece respectively?

A f_o/f_e B f_e/f_o C $f_o \times f_e$ D $f_o + f_e$ E $f_o - f_e$

(objective 11)

5 An astronomical telescope consists of two converging lenses, of focal lengths 1.00 m and 100 mm, separated by a distance of 1.10 m. It is used to view a distant object.

(a) Calculate the angular magnification when it is used in normal adjustment.

(b) What happens to the magnifying power of the telescope if the eyepiece is moved slowly towards the objective?

(c) Calculate the distance between the objective and eyepiece when the final image is formed at the least distance of distinct vision (250 mm).

(d) What is the value of the angular magnification in this new position?

(objective 13)

6 A thin converging lens A of focal length 10.0 cm is arranged at a distance of 20.0 cm from a screen at right angles to the axis of the lens. A thin diverging lens B of focal length 30.0 cm is then placed coaxially between the converging lens and the screen so that the image of an object 30.0 cm from the converging lens is focused on the screen.

(a) Draw a ray diagram to show the passage of two rays of light from the object through the optical system.

(b) Calculate the distance between the two lenses. State the sign convention employed.

(objectives 7 and 13)

7 Describe the optical system of a spectrometer. What adjustments must be made before a spectrum is observed? *(objective 12)*

8 The refracting angle of a prism is 60.0° and the angle of minimum deviation for yellow light is 40.0°.
(a) What is the refractive index of the glass for yellow light?
(b) What is the smallest possible angle of incidence for a ray of this yellow light which is transmitted without total internal reflection?

(objectives 6 and 13)

9 (a) A thin converging lens produces a sharp image of an object on a screen. If the distance between the object and image is d and the magnification obtained is m, find an expression for the focal length of the lens.
(b) In an experiment a series of values of d and m are obtained. What values must be plotted to give a straight line graph, and how may the focal length of the lens be obtained from the graph?

(objectives 8 and 13)

10 Draw labelled ray diagrams to illustrate the methods used to measure the focal length of (i) a thin converging lens with the aid of a plane mirror, and (ii) a thin diverging lens with the aid of a thin converging lens of longer focal length. In each case show how to calculate the result.

(objective 8)

11 A beaker contains water to a depth of 80 mm, and above that a 40 mm layer of oil.
(a) Draw a ray diagram to show how an eye looking vertically down into the beaker sees the image of a point on the bottom of the beaker.

(b) Calculate the distance of this image below the upper surface of the oil. (The refractive indices of water and oil relative to air are respectively 1.33 and 1.45.)

(objective 5)

12 A liquid is placed in a hollow glass prism with thin parallel sided glass walls. The prism is placed on the table of a spectrometer. What two measurements are required in order to determine the refractive index of the liquid relative to air?

(objectives 5 and 12)

13 A telephoto lens system for a camera consists of a converging lens of focal length 6.0 cm, placed 4.0 cm in front of a diverging lens of focal length 3.0 cm. The camera is focused on a distant object. Calculate the total length of the camera, from the converging lens to the photographic plate, when the image of the object is in focus.

(objective 13)

14 EXTENSION
(a) State the relation between the distances of object and image from a thin lens, the radii of curvature of its surfaces and the refractive index of the material of which it is made.
(b) A thin converging lens has surfaces whose radii of curvature are each 500 mm. It is made of glass of refractive index 1.5. What is the focal length of the lens? Two such lenses are placed in contact coaxially and the space between the lenses is filled with water of refractive index 1.33. What will be the focal length of the combination?

(objectives 16 and 18)

15 EXTENSION
Calculate the focal length of a convex mirror which forms an image one-sixth the size of an object which is placed 30 cm from the mirror.

(objective 18)

16 EXTENSION
A camera is marked with a series of f-numbers (2, 2.8, 4, 5.6, 8, 11, 16). Explain what is meant by an f-number and why these particular values are chosen. Explain, with the aid of diagrams, how altering the f-number enables the depth of field to be changed.

(objective 20)

17 EXTENSION
(a) Define angular magnification, as applied to a microscope.
(b) Draw a diagram to show the passage of three rays of light through a compound microscope from a non-axial point, the final image being formed at the least distance of distinct vision. Mark clearly the principal foci of the objective and eyepiece lenses.

(objective 19)

18 EXTENSION
A compound microscope consists of two thin converging lenses, of focal lengths 10 mm and 50 mm. A small object is placed 11 mm from the objective, and the microscope is adjusted so that the final image is formed at the least distance of distinct vision (250 mm) from the eyepiece. Calculate, from first principles, the angular magnification of the instrument.

(objective 13)

Appendix

Revision work

References to relevant chapters of O level text books are given in each section. Use these references in answering the questions and in checking that you understand the relevant pre-requisite objectives. Answers are given in the 'Answers' section for questions marked *.

Section A Wave terms

References:

Abbott   Chapter 26
Ashhurst   Chapter 20
Duncan PTT   Chapter 13

Use the references listed above in answering the following questions.

Q A 1 Define wavelength, frequency and wave speed of a wave.■

Q A 2 Figure A1 shows how the displacement of a particle at a certain distance from the source of vibration varies with time. Copy this graph, and mark the amplitude a of the wave and the period T of the vibration.■

Refer back to pre-requisite objectives 1 and 2 to confirm that you have now achieved these objectives.

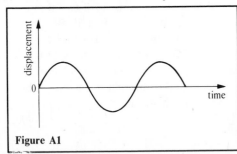

Figure A1

Section B Reflection and refraction

References:

Abbott   Chapters 21, 23 and 25
Ashhurst   Chapters 22, 24 and 28
Duncan PTT   Chapters 1, 2, 3 and 5

Use the references listed above in answering the following questions.

Q A 3 State the laws of reflection of light, and outline how you would test them experimentally.■

Q A 4 Show that the image of a real object in a plane mirror is as far behind the mirror as the object is in front. Outline how you would test this experimentally. What is meant by the statement that this image is virtual.■

Q A 5 Figure A2 shows a point object O in front of two vertical plane mirrors which are placed at right angles to each other. Copy this diagram and complete the paths of two rays from O to show how the images I_1 and I_2 are formed. Mark on your diagram the position of a third image I_3.■

Q A 6 State *four* properties of the image of a real object formed by a plane mirror.■

Q A 7 Show that a ray of light reflected from a plane mirror rotates through an angle of 2θ when the mirror rotates through an angle of θ.■

Q A 8 Explain, with the aid of a diagram, what is meant by refraction. Show on your diagram the incident ray, the refracted ray and the normal, and mark the angle of incidence and the angle of refraction.■

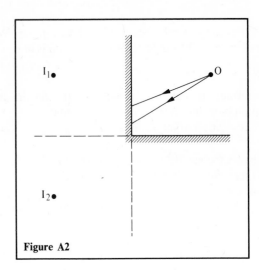

Figure A2

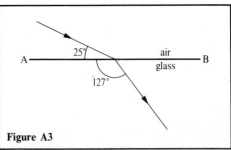

Figure A3

Q A 9 Figure A3 shows the path of a ray of light entering a block of glass.
(a) What is the angle of incidence on the surface AB?
(b) What is the angle of refraction with this surface?■

Q A 10 Explain, with the aid of a diagram, what happens when a narrow beam of white light passes through a triangular glass prism.■

Refer back to pre-requisite objectives 3, 4, 5, 6, 7, 8, and 9 to confirm that you have now achieved these objectives.

Section C Mirrors and lenses

References:

Abbott Chapters 22 and 24
Ashhurst Chapters 23 and 25
Duncan PTT Chapters 4, 7 and 10

Use the references listed above in answering the following questions.

Q A 11 Explain the difference between a real image and a virtual image.■

Q A 12 Show on a ray diagram the centre of curvature C, pole P and principal focus F of a concave mirror.■

Q A 13 Draw ray diagrams to show how, for a real object, a concave mirror forms
(a) an enlarged real image,
(b) a virtual image.■

Q A 14 Copy and complete the following table, to summarise the positions and natures of the images formed by a concave mirror for different positions of the object.

Position of object	Position of image	Nature of image
At infinity	at F	real, inverted, diminished.
Between infinity and C		
At C		
Between C and F		
At F		
Between F and P		

■

Q A 15* An object is placed in front of a concave mirror of focal length 15.0 cm so that it is at right angles to, and has one end resting on, the axis of the mirror. It forms an erect image which is 30.0 cm from the mirror and 6.0 cm high. Find, by graphical construction, the position and height of the object.■

Q A 16 Explain, with the aid of a ray diagram, the terms principal focus F, optical centre C and focal length f as applied to a converging lens.■

Q A 17 Draw ray diagrams to show how, for a real object, a converging lens forms
(a) a real diminished image,
(b) a virtual image.■

Q A 18 Copy and complete the following table, to summarise the positions and natures of the images formed by a converging lens for different positions of a real object (figure A4).

Position of object	Position of image	Nature of image
At infinity	at F_2	real, inverted, diminished.
Between infinity and P		
At P		
Between P and F_1		
At F_1		
Between C and F_1		

■

Q A 19* An object 2.0 cm tall is placed 8.0 cm from a converging lens so that it is at right angles to, and has one end on, the axis of the lens. The object forms a real image 16.0 cm from the lens. Find, by graphical construction,
(a) the focal length of the lens,
(b) the position of the object for which a virtual image is formed equal in size to the former real image.■

Refer back to the pre-requisite objectives 10, 11, 12 and 13 to confirm that you have now achieved these objectives.

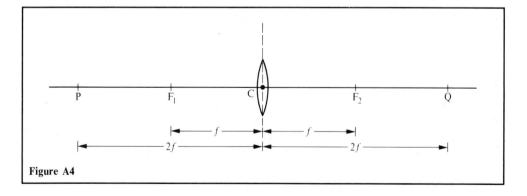

Figure A4

Experiment WP1 Observing wave pulses

Aim

Different types of wave pulse can be observed moving along a stretched spring (or a rubber tube), and the speeds of the pulses estimated.

Apparatus

- stopwatch or stopclock
- metre rule
- long spring
- slinky spring

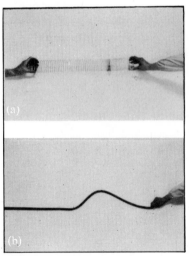

Figure E1

Longitudinal wave pulses

1 Place the slinky spring on a smooth surface. Pull one end of the spring sharply and keep pulling, moving the end at a steady speed. Watch the region of stretched spring spread along the slinky. The coil at the end of the slinky will not be acted on by the pulling force until the wave pulse reaches it. The speed of the moving parts of the spring is not the same as the speed of the wave pulse. What can you say in comparing these speeds?

2 Fix the slinky at one end and extend it along the smooth surface. By momentarily reducing the extension send a compression pulse down the slinky (figure E1a). Observe and describe the motion of one coil of the slinky as a compression wave pulse passes down the slinky. Why is this kind of wave pulse called longitudinal?

Transverse wave pulses

1 Lay the long spring along the floor (a corridor floor is ideal). Stretch the spring by fastening one end to an anchored string or by getting a partner to hold it.

2 Give the end a sideways flick to produce a single transverse pulse, as shown in figure E1b (the pulse is called *transverse* because parts of the spring move *across* the direction in which the pulse travels). Try producing pulses of different shape and ampltiude.

3 Make observations which will enable you to answer the following questions.
(a) What happens to the size and shape of the pulse as it moves down the spring? Why?
(b) What decides the shape of a pulse?
(c) Does the pulse travel with a steady speed?
(d) Can one pulse catch up with another?
(e) What happens to the speed of a pulse if the tension in the spring is increased?
(f) What happens to a pulse when it is reflected from a fixed end?

(g) How does one particular coil move as the pulse passes down the spring? Illustrate your answer by sketching one particular pulse shape you have observed, and a graph showing how the position of a particular coil changes with time as this pulse passes.

4 Observe and describe what happens when two pulses of different shapes are sent along the spring in opposite directions at the same time.

5 Produce a continuous wave by oscillating the spring from side to side at a regular frequency. What happens to the wavelength (distance between adjacent wave crests) as the frequency changes?

6 Vary the frequency of a continuous wave until the waves sent out and reflected back combine to form a wave pattern which does not travel along the spring (this is called a standing wave).

Waves at a boundary

1 Fasten one end of the spring to a taut thread about 3 m long, and observe the reflection of a transverse pulse at this end. How does this compare with reflection at a fixed end?

2 Attach a small mass (e.g. about 100 g of lead) to one of the coils of the slinky or the long spring. This produces a 'discontinuity' in the wave medium (one heavy coil in the midst of many lighter ones). How is the wave energy reflected and transmitted at the discontinuity?

3 Join together the slinky and the long spring, and fix the long spring at its other end. Stretch the free end of the slinky and send a transverse wave pulse down it. Observe and describe what happens after the pulse reaches the boundary.

4 Keeping the springs joined, fix the end of the slinky and send a wave pulse down the long spring towards the slinky. Describe what happens after the pulse reaches the boundary.

Experiment WP2 A study of waves in a ripple tank

Aim

Wave pulses and continuous waves on a water surface are used to obtain evidence about the general properties of waves.

Apparatus

ripple tank kit, including motor, vibrator bar, dippers, reflectors, barriers and small perspex sheet
ripple tank illuminant
white paper screen
hand stroboscope
cell holder and U2 cells
rheostat, 0–15 Ω
leads

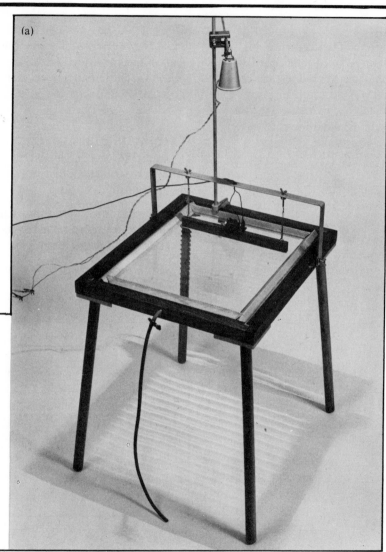

(a)

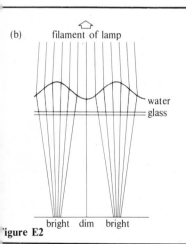

(b)

filament of lamp

water
glass

bright   dim   bright

Figure E2

1 In this experiment you can use your observation of ripples as a model for waves in general. Try throughout to relate your observations to what you already know about the behaviour of sound and light.

2 Set up the ripple tank as in figure E2a, with beaches or absorbers arranged to reduce wave reflection at the sides. Place a lamp about 50 cm above the tank and a white screen on the floor or bench below the tank. Pour in water to a depth of 5 mm. Level the tank. The two images of the lamp, due to reflection at the water surface and at the bottom of the tank, should coincide when the tank is level. Ripples in the tank act as lenses and produce bright and dark areas on the screen below the tank (figure E2b). View the screen directly: do not look through the tank.

3 Observe wave pulses reflected from straight and curved reflectors. A circular wave pulse can be produced by touching the surface lightly or by dropping water from an eye dropper. A plane wave pulse is produced by placing a thick wooden rod in the tank and rolling it forward a little. Remove any bubbles clinging to reflectors in the tank. Record your observations using sketches, commenting on angles of incidence and reflection and the positions of images (sources of reflected waves).

4 Observe the passage of a continuous wave from deep to shallow water. A continuous plane wave is produced by lowering the vibrator bar to touch the water surface. Place a glass or perspex sheet on steel washers in the tank and adjust the water level so that the perspex sheet is only just covered. Use a hand stroboscope to view the image of the ripples, adjusting the speed of rotation until the waves appear stationary.

5 The frequency of the wave remains constant, since the bar is vibrating at constant frequency. What effect has depth on the wavelength and wave velocity? Observe the refraction for different angles of incidence and different frequencies of the vibrator and note any significant observations.

Continued overleaf

6   Place two barriers parallel to the vibrator bar, in line with each other and with a gap of a few centimetres between them. Observe the passage of periodic plane waves through different sizes of aperture. Observe and record how the wave pattern beyond the aperture changes as the gap is narrowed. (The effect you are observing is called diffraction. The waves spread out beyond the aperture.)

7   Adjust the vibrator frequency and note the effect of changing the wavelength on the diffraction pattern. Which waves are diffracted most at a particular aperture, long or short? Is the diffraction effect determined by the actual size of the aperture, or by the size of the aperture relative to the wavelength of the waves? Test your answer by observation. Record any observed variation in the wave intensity (strength of the ripples) in different directions.

8   Fix two dippers to the vibrator bar, about 5 cm apart, and adjust the vibrator bar so that the dippers just dip into the water. Observe the pattern produced when two circular waves are superposed, from the two point sources vibrating in phase and with the same frequency. Sketch the pattern of strong ripples and calm water, and observe the effect on this pattern of (i) changing the frequency of the dippers, (ii) changing the separation of the dippers.

9   Remove one of the dippers and set up a reflector so that it is 3 or 4 cm from the remaining dipper and at right angles to the vibrating bar. Explain how the pattern is produced, and say how the position of the reflector affects the pattern.

Experiment WP3 Speed of sound in air

Aim
The aim of this experiment is to obtain a value for the speed of sound in air by a direct method. You will use a cathode ray oscilloscope to measure the time taken for sound waves to travel a known distance.

Apparatus
- cathode ray oscilloscope
- metre rule
- microphone
- amplifier
- loudspeaker
- leads

Note. If you have not used a cathode ray oscilloscope you should familiarise yourself with its controls before starting the experiment. (The controls of a typical c.r.o. are described in the unit *Electrical properties*. The manufacturer's handbook will give details for the particular oscilloscope you are using.)

Investigating the sweep output

1   An oscilloscope has an output terminal (labelled 'sweep output' or 'probe test') from the calibrated time base. It is this facility that enables this experiment to be carried out.

2   Set up the apparatus as shown in figure E3.1. Connect the sweep output and the earth terminals of the c.r.o. to the input of the amplifier. Connect the output of the amplifier to the loudspeaker.

3   Set the time base at a slow setting (e.g. 100 ms cm^{-1}). What do you observe?

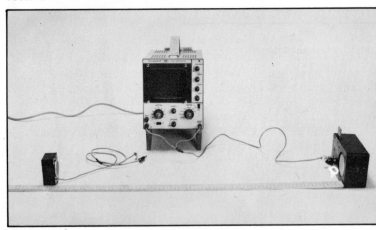

Figure E3.1

Measurement of speed

Connect the microphone to the input and earth terminals of the c.r.o.

Set the Y-gain control to its maximum setting (e.g. 0.1 V cm⁻¹) and the time base at a faster speed (e.g. 1 ms cm⁻¹).

When the microphone is placed close to the loudspeaker a pattern should be obtained on the screen (figure E3.2). Move the microphone away from the loudspeaker. The position of the trace should change. Give a reason for this.
Note. You may have to adjust the gain control of the amplifier.

Move the microphone through a measured distance (e.g. one metre), record the length x on the c.r.o. and hence find the time taken for the sound waves to travel a distance of one metre.

Repeat the experiment several times and find an average value for the speed of sound in air.

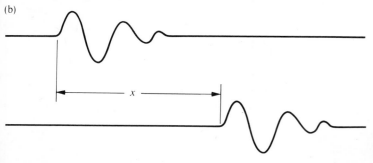

(b)

x

Figure E3.2

Experiment WP4
Interference of sound waves

Aim

In this experiment you will investigate a sound interference pattern and obtain data from which you can estimate the wavelength of sound and calculate the speed of sound in air.

Apparatus
- signal generator
- 2 loudspeakers
- microphone
- cathode ray oscilloscope
- leads
- metre rule

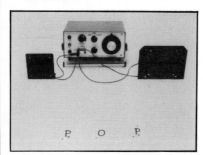

P₁   O   P₂

Figure E4

Note. If possible, carry out this experiment outside the laboratory. If you do carry it out indoors, keep the sound as quiet as possible!

1 Place the two loudspeakers about 2 m apart, as shown in figure E4. Connect them in parallel to the low impedance output of the signal generator. The output of the signal generator should be set at about 400 Hz.

2 Stand at the central position O in front of the loudspeakers, then walk back and forth along a line parallel to a line joining the two speakers, and listen for loud and quiet places. Why does this observation provide evidence for the wave nature of sound?
Note. If the central position O turns out to be a place of minimum intensity, reverse the connections to one of the loudspeakers. This will make it a place of maximum intensity.

3 Locate the first position, P_1, of maximum intensity on one side of O. What can you say about the waves which arrive at P_1 from the two loudspeakers S_1 and S_2? Measure the distances P_1S_1 and P_1S_2, and calculate the path difference $(P_1S_1 - P_1S_2)$. How is this distance related to the wavelength of the sound waves?

4 Using the relationship $c = f\lambda$, estimate a value for the speed of sound in air.

5 Repeat steps 3 and 4 for the first point of maximum intensity, P_2, on the other side of O.

6 Repeat the experiment, using a microphone connected to a c.r.o. to detect the variation in amplitude of the sound at different places about 1 m from the loudspeakers. Arrange the speakers about 0.5 m apart and use a frequency of 4 kHz.

Experiment WP5 Interference of light from two slits

Aim
To obtain an interference pattern using Young's slits and estimate the wavelength of light.

Apparatus
- vertical filament lamp (12 V, 36 W) with stand and shield
- microscope slide
- slide holder for ruling slits
- Aquadag
- needle
- transluscent screen
- adjustable slit
- eyepiece (magnifying glass) and holder
- green filter
- transparent millimetre scale
- leads
- metre rule

In this experiment you have to make your own apparatus for obtaining Young's fringes and measuring the average wavelength of light which passes through a green filter. Setting up the apparatus successfully requires an unusual amount of patience and care, which will be rewarded by obtaining an impressive pattern. These experimental notes are not a step-by-step recipe to obtain fringes, but a series of notes on the experimental set-up. Sometimes alternative approaches are indicated. Read right through the notes and then decide on your own strategy.

1 Constructing a double slit.
(a) The double slit can be ruled on a microscope slide which has been coated with colloidal graphite (Aquadag). Ideally the slide should be coated a few hours before ruling so that the coating is hard. The coating should be opaque, but not too thick. The slide can be placed in a special holder (figure E5.1a), and one slit ruled with a blunt needle or razor blade. Then the screw, with a pitch of 0.5 mm, is used to displace the slide so that a second slit can be ruled. Figure E5.1b shows an alternative method requiring more skill. The slits should not be more than 0.5 mm apart (centre-to-centre). Try to make the two slits of equal width. Wide slits produce a brighter pattern, but few fringes. The widest slit allowable, for a reasonable pattern, will be of width equal to half the slit separation (i.e. slits of width x with an opaque region of width x between them). Several pairs of slits can be ruled on the same slide, and tested by holding the slide to your eye and looking at a distant line filament lamp. This will enable you to judge brightness, definition and separation for fringes produced by different double slits.

(b) An alternative arrangement for producing a double slit is shown in figure E5.1c. A length of bare copper wire, s.w.g. 26, is stretched until it gives. A piece of this wire is glued across a hole in a piece of tin plate. The positions of the razor blades are adjusted to produce two narrow slits of equal width.

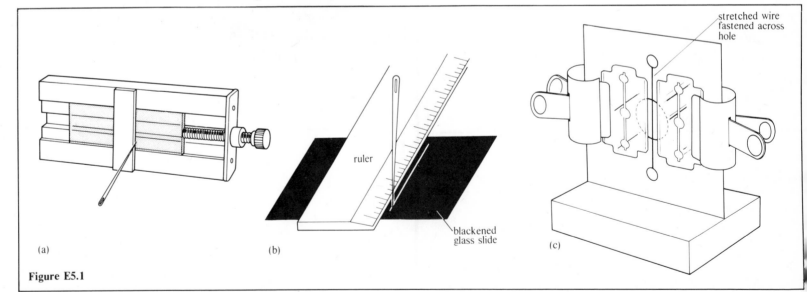

(a)　　　　　　(b)　ruler　blackened glass slide　　(c) stretched wire fastened across hole

Figure E5.1

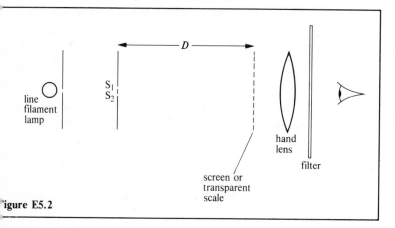

line filament lamp

S_1
S_2

D

hand lens

filter

screen or transparent scale

Figure E5.2

Making a slit source

e source is a lamp with a vertical line filament. A shield around the
mp prevents stray light reaching the screen. An adjustable slit,
rmed between two razor blades, should be placed in front of the
ament lamp to increase the definition of the pattern.

Arranging the apparatus.

ake sure the lamp, slits and viewing screen (or lens) are in line, and
at the filament and all the slits are parallel to each other (figure E5.2).
e distance from the source to the double slits should be about 1 metre.
e distance D from the double slits to the screen determines the
paration of the fringes. It must be two or more metres when the slit
paration is 0.5 mm, but if the slits are closer together the viewing
tance can be less. If a lens is used to magnify the pattern, the distance
can be reduced to as little as 30 cm. When the fringes are clearly
ible, hold a green filter in front of your eye. Two factors which may
vent you obtaining a good pattern are (i) having slit S too wide, and
making slits S_1 and S_2 unequal in width. Take care to eliminate
se factors.

4   Viewing the pattern.

A translucent screen can be used to view the fringes. Alternatively, a
magnifying glass or microscope eyepiece can be used to view fringes
located just in front of the lens, in the object plane. Stray light can be
reduced by placing the screen at the end of a box or long tube blackened
on the inside. (A travelling microscope with the objective lens removed
provides a viewing lens and a tube to reduce stray light.)

5   Taking measurements.

(a) The fringe separation x (the distance from the centre of one dark
fringe to the centre of the next dark fringe) can be found by (i) marking
on the screen the location of the dark fringes at the edges of the pattern,
(ii) placing the transparent scale in front of the viewing lens, so that the
scale divisions are in sharp focus and superimposed on the fringe
pattern formed in the same plane as the scale. Alternatively, a travelling
microscope can be used.

(b) The slit separation can be found by (i) placing the transparent scale
across or alongside the slide and looking at the slits and the scale
through a magnifying glass or microscope, or (ii) using a travelling
microscope, or (iii) placing the lamp just behind the double slits and
using a lens to obtain a magnified image of the slits on a screen.

6   Calculating the wavelength.

The wavelength λ of the light forming the fringes is given by the
equation $\lambda = dx/D$, where d is the slit separation, x the fringe separation
and D the distance from slits to fringes. Obtain a value for the average
wavelength transmitted by the filter. State briefly how you measured
each of the quantities in the above equation, and estimate the possible
percentage error in each quantity. (Section 9 of the Student's Handbook
is about estimating experimental errors.) Write down your answer for
the value of wavelength λ, stating the estimated experimental error and
giving the correct number of significant figures.

Experiment WP6 Refractive index by apparent depth

Aim
You will use a travelling microscope to measure the refractive index of a glass block.

Apparatus
- travelling microscope
- 2 rectangular glass blocks
- lycopodium powder

Figure E6

1 Place one glass block on the bench and sprinkle lycopodium powder (or chalk dust) on its upper surface. Arrange the travelling microscope so that it is vertically above the lycopodium (figure E6).

2 Adjust the cross-wires of the microscope so that they can be seen without strain.

3 Focus the microscope on the lycopodium powder (using the fine adjustment screw to obtain a sharp focus) and read the vertical vernier scale, d_1.

4 Place the second glass block on top of the first one (without removing the lycopodium powder) and adjust the height of the microscope until the lycopodium powder is again in focus. Read the vernier scale, d_2.

5 Sprinkle some more lycopodium powder on the upper surface of the second glass block. Adjust the height of the microscope until this lycopodium powder is in focus. Read the vernier scale, d_3.

6 Turn the second glass block over and repeat the measurements.

7 Calculate a mean value of the refractive index of the glass block. The refractive index n is given by

$$n = \frac{\text{real thickness}}{\text{apparent thickness}} = \frac{d_3 - d_1}{d_3 - d_2}.$$

8 Investigate the error in focusing the microscope, and estimate the percentage error in each reading.

9 Calculate the percentage error in your value for the refractive index.

10 Outline how you would use a similar method to measure the refractive index of a liquid.

Experiment WP7 Refractive index by critical angle

Aim

The aim of this experiment is to measure the refractive index of a small quantity of liquid.

Apparatus

rectangular glass block
4 optical pins
drawing board
drawing pins
protractor
white paper
liquid (e.g. glycerol or paraffin)

Measurement of refractive index of glass block

1   Fasten the paper to the drawing board, place the glass block in the centre and mark its outline ABCD.

2   Place two pins, P_1 and P_2, into the board as shown in figure E7.1.

3   Look through side BC of the glass block and observe the images of pins P_1 and P_2. Place two more pins, P_3 and P_4, so that they appear to be in line with the image I_1 and I_2 of pins P_1 and P_2. The four pins represent the path along which a ray of light would pass through the block.

4   Mark the positions of the pins. Remove the pins and the block and draw in the path of the ray of light.

5   Measure the angles of incidence and refraction on both sides of the block. Calculate the value of the refractive index of glass, n_g.

6   Repeat the experiment with different angles of incidence and find an average value for the refractive index.

Measurement of critical angle

1   Fasten a second piece of paper to the drawing board, place the glass block in the centre and mark the outline ABCD.

2   Cut a strip of paper about 2 mm wide, of length equal to the height of the block. Draw a line along it and smear this side of the paper with the liquid. Place it on the side AD, about a quarter of the way from A to D, at L_1 (figure E7.2), so that the line is vertical.

3   Look into the side CD with your eye near to C. Then move your eye nearer to D. What do you notice about the line on the paper?

4   Place two pins P_1 and P_2 to mark the direction beyond which the line cannot be seen.

5   Remove the glass block. Join P_1 and P_2 to meet the side CD at M. Join LM and measure the critical angle c.

6   Alter the position of the paper on the glass block (you may need to resmear it with liquid), place the glass block in a different position and repeat steps 4 and 5. Calculate a mean value for the critical angle.

7   By applying the formula $n_1 \sin i_1 = n_2 \sin i_2$, at L and M respectively, show that

$$n_1 = n_g \ \sin c$$

where n_1 is the refractive index of the liquid and n_g is the refractive index of the glass.

8   Calculate a value for the refractive index of the liquid.

9   Repeat the experiment with water and one other liquid.

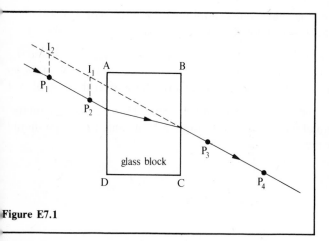

Figure E7.1

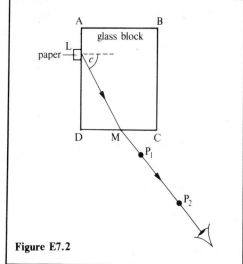

Figure E7.2

Experiment WP8 The converging lens

Aim

In this experiment you will determine the focal length of a converging lens using an auxiliary plane mirror and a graphical method.

Apparatus

- converging lens and holder
- plane mirror
- cross-wires
- lamp and holder
- screen
- metre rule

Figure E8

Using an auxiliary plane mirror

1 First find an approximate value for the focal length of the lens by focusing the image of a distant object (e.g. a laboratory window) on the screen. Measure the distance between the lens and the screen. This is a rough value of the focal length of the lens.

2 Place the illuminated cross wires at a distance from the lens equal to the approximate focal length and position the plane mirror behind the lens, normal to the principal axis (figure E8).

3 Adjust the position of the cross-wires until a sharp image of the cross-wires is formed alongside them.

4 Measure the distance of the cross-wires from the optical centre of the lens. This is the focal length f of the lens.

5 Repeat steps 3 and 4 several times and find the mean of the results.

6 Explain, with the aid of a ray diagram, why the distance from the object to the lens is equal to the focal length of the lens when the object and image coincide.

7 Does the position of the plane mirror make any difference to your result? Give a reason.

Graphical method

1 Place the illuminated cross-wires at a distance from the lens of approximately $2f$. Adjust the position of the screen so that there is a sharp image on the screen.

2 Measure the distances of the object, u, and the image, v, from the lens.

3 Move the object 2 cm nearer the lens and locate the new position of the image. Obtain at least five sets of readings of the object distance and the image distance.

4 Plot graphs of (i) v (y-axis) against u (x-axis), and (ii) $1/v$ (y-axis) against $1/u$ (x-axis). Comment on these graphs and explain what you think they show.
Note. You may have to take additional readings to obtain appropriately spaced points on these graphs.

5 What is the value of v when $u = v$? How is this value related to the focal length of the lens? How can you obtain the focal length of the lens from the graph of v against u? Write down the answer that you obtain.

6 What is the value of $1/v$ when $1/u$ is zero? How can you obtain the focal length of the lens from the graph of $1/v$ against $1/u$? (You should obtain the mean of two values.)

Experiment WP9 The astronomical telescope

im

this experiment you will set up
nple type of astronomical
escope and estimate the
ignification produced.

im

this experiment you will set up
nple type of astronomical
escope and estimate the
ignification produced.

pparatus
long focal length converging
lens (50 cm)
short focal length converging
lens (10 cm)
suitable mounting rod
metre rule
low voltage lamp and power
supply
tissue paper or greaseproof
paper
screen

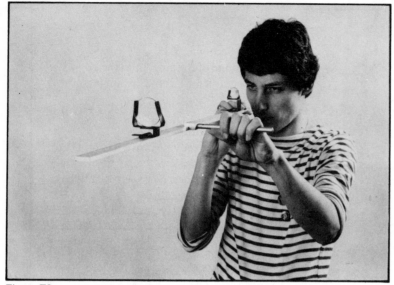

Figure E9

Constructing the telescope

1   Determine the focal lengths of each lens by focusing the image of a
distant object on a screen.

2   Place a lamp at the far side of the laboratory. Mount the lens with
the longer focal length at one end of the mounting rod. Point the rod at
the lamp and locate the image of the lamp on a piece of greaseproof
paper.

3   Attach the second lens near the other end of the mounting rod.
Adjust the position of this lens so that it acts as a magnifying glass for
the image on the greaseproof paper.

4   Remove the greaseproof paper and look directly at the image of the
lamp formed by the telescope (figure E9).

Estimating the magnification

1   Rule several horizontal lines, 2 cm apart, on a sheet of paper or a
blackboard. Illuminate the lines with a lamp.

2   Point the telescope towards the ruled lines (which should be on the
far side of the laboratory) and adjust the position of the eyepiece until
the lines can be seen clearly.

3   Look through the telescope with one eye and look directly at the
lines with the other (unaided) eye. Make final adjustments to the
eyepiece until the eye looking through the telescope sees the image
clearly in focus, while the unaided eye sees the lines clearly in focus. You
must make a conscious effort to relax your eyes. Don't give up
immediately!

4   Count how many lines, as viewed directly, lie between two adjacent
lines as seen through the telescope. Hence estimate the magnification
produced by the telescope.

5   Compare your results with the value obtained from the formula
$$\text{angular magnification} = \frac{\text{focal length of objective}}{\text{focal length of eyepiece}},$$
which gives the value for the angular magnification if both the object
and image are an infinite distance from the eye (normal adjustment).

Locating the eye ring

1   Place a piece of greaseproof paper (or a frosted glass screen) close
to the objective. Illuminate it with light from a lamp, and position a
piece of white card behind the eyepiece. You should observe a circle of
light.

2   Adjust the position of the card until the circle has a sharp outline.
Of what is the circle the image?

3   Measure the diameter d of this image and the diameter D of the
objective lens. Find the ratio D/d. This ratio is numerically equal to the
angular magnification of the telescope, when it is in normal adjustment.

Answers

Chapter 1

1.1 (a) The water level is forced down by the stone where it hits, but the level around the stone rises.
(b) Intermolecular forces, including surface tension forces.
(c) See figure 1.31.
(d) Kinetic energy is transferred to the particles of the water and spreads out through the water as the ripples move.
(e) The moving water particles have inertia. They overshoot the equilibrium position and vibrate, exchanging potential energy and kinetic energy.

1.2 (a) No. The disturbance is not handed on from the source through the medium.
(b) The pulse of starting travels backwards. Its speed depends on the reaction times of the drivers and the distance between cars as they queue.

1.3 (a) To the right.
(b) Yes, to the left.
(c) No. It is only possible to say which way it is moving at instant 7 if we have information about its position at instant 8 as well as instant 6.

1.4 (a) Longitudinal.
(b) Transverse, longitudinal, torsional.

1.5 A displacement – time graph.

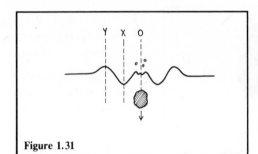

Figure 1.31

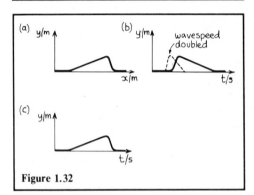

Figure 1.32

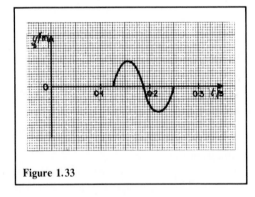

Figure 1.33

1.6 See figure 1.32.

1.7 (a) See figure 1.33.
(b) The slope of the tangent to the y against t graph for P is the instantaneous velocity of P.

1.8 (a) See figure 1.34.
(b) A and B are moving down, C and D are moving up.
(c) A has the greatest average speed, B has the least average speed.
(d) At the peak of the pulse.

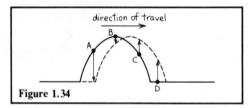

Figure 1.34

1.10 (a) See figure 1.35.
(b) O is always at rest.
(c) At this instant all the energy is in the form of kinetic energy of the string. Although the string is undisplaced it has maximum kinetic energy: part is moving up, and part moving down.

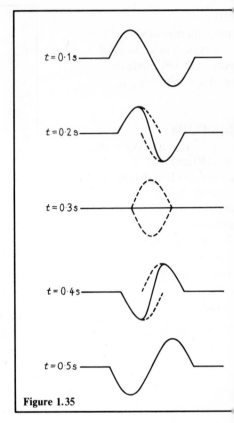

Figure 1.35

11 (a) Two approaching pulses, [su]perposed at instant 5, mean that the [occ]urred section of the spring is moving up. [Th]e pulses are travelling away from each [ot]her at instant 7, and must be moving [do]wn.
[(b)] The pulses completely overlap, so the [pa]rticle displacements are maximum. [Pa]rticles of the spring move up in the [le]ading half of a pulse and down in the [fo]llowing half. When the pulses overlap [th]e particle velocities are equal and [op]posite, with a zero resultant.
[(c)] The amplitude of the pulses is less at [th]e bottom than at the top. Some of the [wa]ve energy has been dissipated in heating [th]e spring.

[1]2 When the pulse reaches the support, [th]e leading part exerts an upward force on [th]e support. The support will therefore [ex]ert a force on the spring in the opposite [di]rection, downwards.

[1]3 (a) From measurements of the [di]stances travelled by the pulses after [tra]nsmission and reflection, the speed in [th]e light spring is three times that in the [he]avy spring.
[(b)] More wave energy will be reflected and [les]s transmitted.
No.

1.16 (a) See figure 1.36.
(b) The velocity is given by the gradient of the tangent to the $y - t$ curve.
(c) The gradient, and therefore the velocity, is maximum when the displacement is zero. The gradient is zero when the particle has maximum displacement.
(d) No. Particles with the same displacement may have identical velocities or equal and opposite velocities.

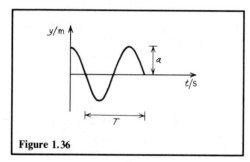

Figure 1.36

1.17 (a) (i) A and B, C and D;
(ii) A and D, B and C; (iii) A and E.
(b) A and B are moving at the same speed but in opposite directions.
(c) A and E.
(d) One wavelength. As V moves up and down once, a crest at a particular point will be replaced first by a trough and then by the next crest.
(e) 2.4 m s⁻¹. AE is the distance from one crest to the next, and is therefore one wavelength. The wave travels 1.2 m in 0.5 s.

1.18 (a) Amplitude, frequency (and hence period).
(b) In phase is used to describe vibrations which are in step. Points like A and E have the same displacement and velocity at the same instant, so they are vibrating in phase. As the wave travels along, point B reaches its maximum upward displacement after point A. The vibration of B lags behind the vibration of A, so B has a phase lag behind A.
(c) A and E are consecutive points which are in phase. There will be another point, an equal distance to the right of E, which is also in phase with A and E.

1.19 (a) f is the number of wavelengths passing a fixed point per second, so the distance travelled per second by the waveform = frequency × wavelength.
(b) The wavelength would be increased.
(c) 2×10^5 Hz (200 kHz).

1.20 See figure 1.37.

1.22 See figure 1.38. The amplitude is 10 mm, the period is 12 s, and when $t = 7$ s, $y = -5$ mm.

1.23 (a) When $t = 0$, $y = a \sin(-\pi/2)$
$$= -a.$$
When $t = \pi/2\omega$, $y = a \sin 0 = 0$.
When $t = \pi/\omega$, $y = a \sin(\pi/2) = a$.

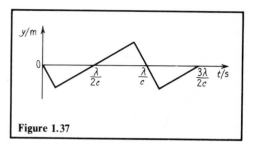

Figure 1.37

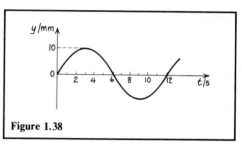

Figure 1.38

(b) Q is the point represented. It has displacement $y = -a$ when $t = 0$, and moves up after this instant.
(c) See figure 1.39.
(d) Phase lag for R $= \pi$,
equation for R is $y = a \sin(\omega t - \pi)$.
When $t = 0$, $y = a \sin(-\pi) = 0$.
When $t = \pi/2\omega$, $y = a \sin(-\pi/2) = -a$.
Phase lag for S $= 3\pi/2$,
equation for S is $y = a \sin \{\omega t - (3\pi/2)\}$.
When $t = 0$, $y = a \sin(-3\pi/2) = -a$.
When $t = \pi/2\omega$, $y = a \sin(-\pi) = 0$.
(e) It is greater than $3\pi/2$.

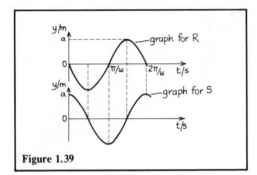

Figure 1.39

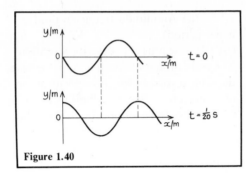

Figure 1.40

1.24 (a) $y = a \sin(\omega t - \phi)$.
(b) $y = a \sin(\omega t - kx)$.
(c) $kx = 2\pi$ when $x = \lambda$, so $k = 2\pi/\lambda$.
(d) $y = a \sin 2\pi \{(t/T) - (x/\lambda)\}$.
(e) $y = a \sin 2\pi f \{t - (x/c)\}$.

1.25 (a) $f = 5$ Hz.
(b) $\lambda = 4/5$ m $= 80$ cm.
(c) 4 m s^{-1} (using $c = f\lambda$).
(d) See figure 1.40.
(e) When $x = 2$ m, $y = a \sin(\omega t - 5\pi)$ or $y = a \sin(\omega t - \pi)$.
(f) $y = 0$ when $t = 0$. The vibrator was moving up.
(g) $y = 0.05 \sin \pi (10t + 2.5\,x)$ metres.

1.26 See figure 1.41.

1.27 See figure 1.42.

1.28 (a) Spherical.
(b) As a circle.
(c) Cylindrical.
(d) As circles.

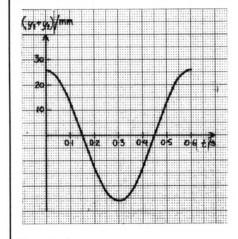

Figure 1.41

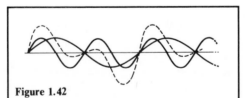

Figure 1.42

1.29 (a) In the direction opposite to that of the incident pulse.
(b) The pulse is still reflected back in the direction opposite to that of the incident pulse.

1.30 (a) Both pulses are travelling away from the reflector (to the left).
The circular wave is travelling directly from the point source.
The plane wave pulse is the reflected wave front.
(b) The plane wave contains all the reflected energy, which has been radiated from the source into a larger angle than the direct wave. Also, the smaller amount of energy is distributed over a longer wavefront in the circular wave. Hence ripples in the circular wave are smaller than those in the plane wave.
(c) Approximately one-third.

1.31 Ripples travel more slowly in shallow water than in deep water. As the ripple is travelling faster towards B and slower towards D, the water depth must increase towards B and decrease towards D. Corner B is tilted down and corner D tilted up.

1.32 The wave energy is concentrated around the headland, producing waves of large amplitude (figure 1.43). The energy of the wave is less concentrated in the bay, producing waves of smaller amplitude (calmer water).

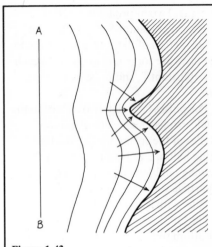

Figure 1.43

1.33 The ripples of lower frequency (figure 1.26a) have been refracted most.

1.35 For long wavelength waves the term containing surface tension γ is negligible. hence $v^2 = g\lambda/2\pi$.
When $\lambda = 10$ m, $v_{10} = 10 \times 10/2 = 4.0$ m s^{-1}
When $\lambda = 20$ m, $v_{20} = 10 \times 20/2 = 5.6$ m s^{-1}
If the time to reach land is t_{10} for short waves and t_{20} for long waves,

$$t_{10} = \frac{2 \times 10^6 \text{ m}}{4.0 \text{ m s}^{-1}} = 0.50 \times 10^6 \text{ s},$$

$$t_{20} = \frac{2 \times 10^6 \text{ m}}{5.6 \text{ m s}^{-1}} = 0.36 \times 10^6 \text{ s}.$$

me difference $= 1.4 \times 10^5$ s $\approx 1\frac{1}{2}$ days.
The bigger waves (the giant rollers) are the first waves to hit the coast by a significant margin. It is these waves which produce the sudden devastation and flooding at the coast.

36 (a) The dark circles represent points where two crests meet. The water level is raised by the sum of the amplitudes of the superposed waves.
(b) Half a period later, the dark circle points will be at the bottom of deep troughs.
(c) The water level oscillates between a high crest and a low trough. This is true for each point marked with a dark circle, though the crests and troughs diminish as the wave energy spreads out.
(d) The points marked with blank circles have the same amplitude of vibration as those marked with dark circles. They are, however, out of phase by π rad (opposite phase).
(e) The line of dark and blank circles marks the line along which the surface vibrates with maximum amplitude.
(f) Path difference at P $= \lambda$. It is the same for all points along line A_1.
(g) Path difference $= n\lambda$ ($n = 0, 1, 2, \ldots$).
(h) At these points the water will be relatively undisturbed, since a crest and a trough meet at the instant recorded. This will also be true half a period or a whole

period later. The vibration at these points has minimum amplitude, and the lines joining these points are nodal lines.
(i) Path difference at R $= 5\lambda/2$, and this is the path difference along line N_3. The path difference along line N_4 is $7\lambda/2$.

1.37 (i) The nodal lines radiate from a point midway between the sources, suggesting that $x \propto D$.
(ii) As the source separation d decreases, the separation x of adjacent nodes (calm water) increases. Measurements of photographs 1.23a and 1.23c support the idea that $x \propto 1/d$, because xd is constant.
(iii) Photographs 1.23a and 1.23b show that, for a constant separation of the sources, the distance x between nodes decreases as the wavelength decreases. This suggests that $x \propto \lambda$.
A possible relationship is $x \propto (\lambda D/d)$.

1.38 (a) 0.75 cm. The wavelength is 3 cm, and for this node the path lengths are 3.75 cm and 5.25 cm, producing a path difference of 1.5 cm (half a wavelength).
(b) Six (see figure 1.44).
(c) The positions of the nodal points will change, but their separation will still be 1.5 cm. There will now be a node halfway between the sources, and four other nodes along the line between the sources.
(d) There will be no steady interference pattern. There will still be nodes and

antinodes, but their positions will change. Every ten seconds the sources will be in step and will produce a pattern like that in part (b). Five seconds later the pattern will be like that in part (c).

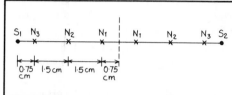

Figure 1.44

Chapter 2

2.1 (a) 1.7×10^{-2} m (highest frequency), and 17 m (lowest frequency).
(b) 3.3×10^{-6} m.

2.2 (a) BD represents particle displacement to the left, AB and DF displacements to the right.
(b) B and F.
(c) O and D.
(d) A, C and E.
(e) See figure 2.10.

2.3 (i) The personal equation of the observer, that is, the time lag between the observer seeing the flash and operating the timing device.

(ii) The effect of the wind. This can be reduced by taking reciprocal observations (that is, by taking readings for the sound travelling in opposite directions over the same distance at the same time).
(iii) Variable and unknown conditions in the atmosphere over long distances. Temperature and humidity vary locally, and it is not possible to allow for this.

2.4 (a) The volume doubles.
(b) The density is halved.
(c) p/ρ remains the same. The speed of sound does not depend on pressure.

2.5 Speed of sound $= 3.3 \times 10^2$ m s^{-1}.
Using $c = \sqrt{\gamma p/\rho}$,

$$c = \sqrt{\frac{1.4 \times 1.0 \times 10^{15}\,\text{Pa}}{1.3\,\text{kg m}^{-3}}}$$

$$= 3.3 \times 10^2\,\text{m s}^{-1}.$$

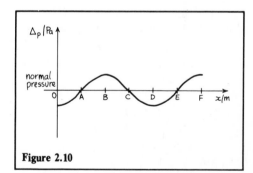

Figure 2.10

2.6 0.6 m s^{-1} per °C rise in temperature. For a 1°C rise in temperature, since

$$c \propto \sqrt{T},$$

$$\frac{\text{velocity at 1 °C}}{\text{velocity at 0 °C}} = \sqrt{\frac{274}{273}}$$

velocity at 1 °C $= 330.6 \text{ m s}^{-1}$.
(Alternatively, using calculus, since $c = kT^{\frac{1}{2}}$, where k is a constant,

$$\frac{dc}{dT} = \tfrac{1}{2}kT^{-\frac{1}{2}}$$

$$= \tfrac{1}{2}\left(\frac{c}{T^{\frac{1}{2}}}\right)T^{-\frac{1}{2}}$$

$$= \tfrac{1}{2}\left(\frac{c}{T}\right).$$

Therefore $\delta c \approx \tfrac{1}{2}\left(\frac{c}{T}\right)\delta T$

$$= \tfrac{1}{2} \times \frac{330}{273} \times 1 \text{ m s}^{-1}$$

$$= 0.6 \text{ m s}^{-1}.)$$

2.8 The frequency heard is 735.5 Hz: the note is about 1.5 octaves higher than in air. Using $c = \sqrt{\gamma p/\rho}$ and $c = f\lambda$, and assuming that the pressure of the gas in the lungs is constant,

$$\frac{f_h}{f_a} = \frac{c_h}{c_a} = \sqrt{\left(\frac{\gamma_h p}{\rho_h}\right)\left(\frac{\rho_a}{\gamma_a p}\right)}$$

$$f_h = 256\sqrt{\frac{1.6 \times 1.3}{0.18 \times 1.4}} \text{ Hz}$$

$$= 735.5 \text{ Hz}.$$

2.9 To produce a distinct image, a surface must treat all parts of the advancing wavefront similarly. It must not introduce a path difference for different parts of the wavefront, and must therefore not have irregularities greater than a fraction of the wavelength. For sound, with wavelengths of the order of 1 m, the reflecting surface can have irregularities of several centimetres and still produce a distinct sound image. For light, with wavelengths of about 500 nm, the reflecting surface must be highly polished to remove all irregularities greater than a few nanometres.

2.11 The wind velocity is added vectorially to that of sound, and since the wind velocity increases with height the effect is to distort the wavefronts as shown in figure 2.11. There is greater audibility down-wind at D than up-wind at U.

2.12 (a) The distance between maxima will be increased.
(b) The phase difference is equivalent to introducing a path difference of $\lambda/2$, so the central point of the interference pattern will become a minimum, the positions of the previous minima will become maxima, and so on.

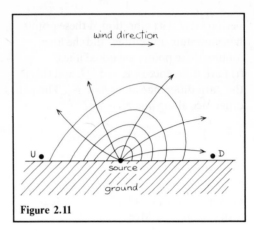

Figure 2.11

2.15 (a) 252 Hz and 260 Hz.
(b) Adjust the tension of the piano string (to change the frequency of the note) so that the beat frequency decreases. When the string is tuned there will be no beats.

2.18 Observed change in frequency is 250 Hz.
As the source approaches,

$$f_o = f_s\left(\frac{c}{c - v_s}\right)$$

$$= f_s\left(\frac{c}{c - c/5}\right)$$

$$= \tfrac{5}{4}f_s.$$

As the source recedes,

$$f_o = f_s\left(\frac{c}{c + v_s}\right)$$

$$= f_s\left(\frac{c}{c + c/5}\right)$$

$$= \tfrac{5}{6}f_s.$$

Change in frequency $= \left(\tfrac{5}{4} - \tfrac{5}{6}\right)f_s$

$$= \tfrac{5}{12}f_s$$

$$= 250 \text{ Hz}.$$

2.19 (a) $f_o = f_s\left(\dfrac{c}{c - v_s \cos \theta}\right)$

(b) $f_o = f_s$

(c) $f_o = f_s\left(\dfrac{c}{c + v_s \cos \theta}\right)$

2.20 (a) The observed frequency f_o is given by

$$f_o = f_s\left(\frac{c}{c - v_s \cos \theta}\right)$$

therefore $f_o = \dfrac{500 \times 340}{(340 - 60 \cos \theta)}$ Hz.

When the train is a distance x from N (figure 2.12a),

$$\cos \theta = \frac{x}{\sqrt{(50^2 + x^2)}}.$$

Substituting for x, and hence θ, gives the following values.

x/m	$60\cos\theta$/m s^{-1}	f_s/Hz
200	58.2	603
100	53.7	594
50	42.4	571
20	22.3	535
0	0	500

b) When the train is receding, the following values are obtained.

x/m	f_o/Hz
− 20	469
− 50	444
− 100	432
− 200	427

The graph is shown in figure 2.12b.
c) The curve is shown by the dotted line in figure 2.12b.

22   (a) (i) ∞, (ii) 500 Hz.
(b) (i) 2000 Hz, (ii) 0.
(c) If the source travels at the speed of sound, no sound is heard until the source passes the observer, who at that instant receives an intense shock wave. After the source has passed a sound of frequency 250 Hz is heard. An observer approaching the source at the speed of sound hears a sound of twice the emitted frequency. An observer receding from the source at the speed of sound cannot receive any of the emitted sound.

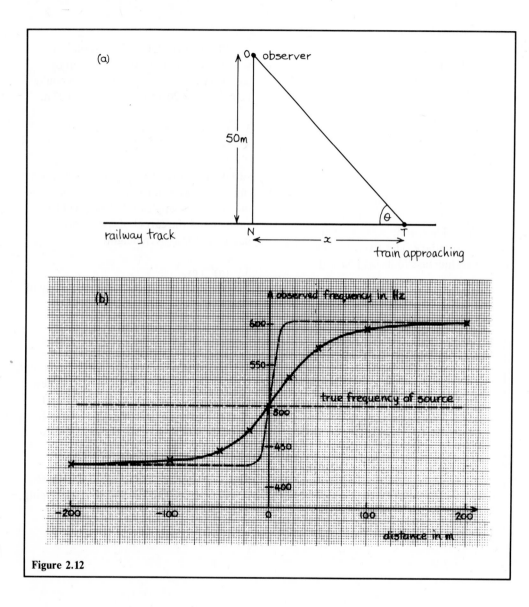

(a) observer
50m
railway track
N
x
θ
T
train approaching

(b) observed frequency in Hz
600
550
true frequency of source
500
450
400
−200
−100
0
100
200
distance in m

Figure 2.12

2.23   The beat frequency is 12 Hz. The beats are produced by the superposition of two waves, one from the receding car horn and one reflected from the wall. The reflected wave appears to be coming from an image of the horn, approaching the observer.
For the wave from the receding horn,

$$f_o = f_s \left(\frac{c}{c + v_s} \right)$$
$$= 400 \times \frac{340}{345} \text{ Hz} = 394 \text{ Hz}.$$

For the wave reflected from the wall,

$$f_o = f_s \left(\frac{c}{c - v_s} \right)$$
$$= 400 \times \frac{340}{335} \text{ Hz} = 406 \text{ Hz}.$$

The beat frequency is the difference between these two frequencies.

2.24 (a) As the satellite moves from position 1 to position 2 the beat frequency decreases. When it is overhead, at position 2, the beat frequency is zero. As the satellite moves from position 2 to position 3 the beat frequency increases.

(b) For a source approaching a stationary observer,

$$f_o = f_s \left(\frac{c}{c - v_s} \right)$$

$$f_o = \frac{f_s}{(1 - v_s/c)}$$

$$f_o - f_o (v_s/c) = f_s$$

$$f_o - f_s = f_o (v_s/c)$$

$$\frac{\Delta f}{f_o} = \frac{v_s}{c}$$

Assuming $f_o \approx f_s$, $\quad \dfrac{\Delta f}{f_s} \approx \dfrac{v_s}{c}$.

2.26 10 m s^{-1}.

$$\text{Frequency of microwaves} = \frac{3 \times 10^8 \text{ m s}^{-1}}{100 \times 10^{-3} \text{ m}}$$

$$= 3 \times 10^9 \text{ Hz}.$$

For a moving reflecting surface, if v is the speed of the car,

$$\Delta f = \left(\frac{2v}{c} \right) f_s,$$

$$v = \frac{c \, \Delta f}{2 f_s}$$

$$= \frac{3 \times 10^8 \times 200}{2 \times 3 \times 10^9} \text{ m s}^{-1}$$

$$= 10 \text{ m s}^{-1}.$$

Chapter 3

3.4 $\quad \dfrac{n_2}{n_1} = \dfrac{c/c_2}{c/c_1} = \dfrac{c_1}{c_2} = {_1}n_2,$

$$_2 n_1 = \frac{c_2}{c_1} = \frac{1}{c_1/c_2} = \frac{1}{{_1}n_2}$$

3.5 (a) ${_1}n_2 = 1.5$

(b) The wavefronts in medium 2 have the same curvature as the boundary, so they will emerge without any change in curvature. There is no refraction at the second boundary. The wavelength will, however, increase to its original value.

3.6 See figure 3.13.

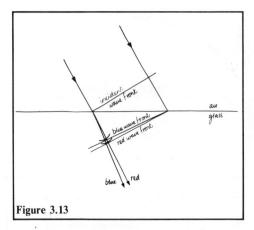

Figure 3.13

3.7 Plot n against $1/\lambda$. The graph is a straight line, so the data agree with the equation $n = A + B/\lambda$. The origin could be at $n = 1.620$ and $1/\lambda = 15 \times 10^5 \text{ m}^{-1}$.

3.8 (a) AE represents a distance $2ct$.

(b)–(e) See figure 3.14a.

(f) The wavefront is a moving conical surface with the moving plane at the apex (figure 3.14b). If the plane's speed is increased, the angle of the cone will be smaller and the carpet of sonic boom narrower for a given height.

3.9 (a) Yes.

(b) They must have the same frequency of vibration and a constant phase relationship.

(c) Yes, they are coherent and would produce a steady pattern.

(d) The flute players would have a different but constant phase relationship, so a new pattern would be set up. The nodes and antinodes would be in different places from those in (c), but with the same separation.

(e) No. Players taking random pauses for breath would produce waves whose frequencies were the same, but the phase relationship would be constantly changing.

3.10 (a) TS$_2$ represents the path difference at P.

(b) Triangle S$_1$PT is an isosceles triangle, so the line PM bisecting the base S$_1$T is also perpendicular to the base.

(c) MP will rotate to the position MO.

(d) Angle θ = angle S$_2$S$_1$T.

(e) Angle S$_1$TS$_2$ is one of the equal base angles of the isosceles triangle S$_1$PT. Since angle S$_1$PT is *very* small, each base angle is approximately 90° (Angle S$_1$PT is less than 0.001 radians (0.06°) for apparatus of the dimensions given.)

(f) Triangles TS$_1$S$_2$ and OMP are similar since they have equal angles.

(g) The distance x is very small compared with D, so PM $\approx$ OM. Therefore TS$_2$/S$_1$S$_2$ = OP/OM, and substituting in this equation gives $p/d = x/D$, or $p = dx/D$.

(h) The approximations can be justified by considering typical experimental values. If $x = 1$ cm and $D = 1$ m, $\theta = 0.01$ radian or 0° 36'. Since OP = MP cos θ, OP = MP $\times$ 0.9999 (using 4 figure tables).

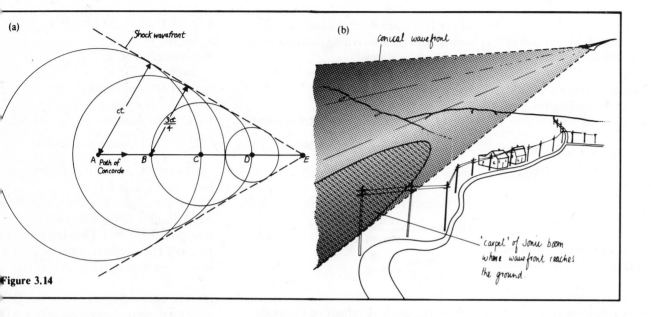

Figure 3.14

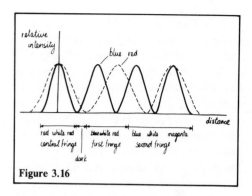

Figure 3.16

3.1 (a) Path difference for the first bright fringe $= \lambda$. Therefore $dx_1/D = \lambda$, or $x_1 = \lambda D/d$.

For the second bright fringe, the path difference is 2λ, so $x_2 = 2\lambda D/d$.

$x_n = n\lambda D/d$.

$x_{n+1} = (n + 1)\lambda D/d$.

Separation $= x_{n+1} - x_n = \lambda D/d$.

Fringe separation is independent of n, the fringes are equidistant and parallel the original slits.

3.2 The fringe separation x is $\times 10^{-4}$ m, so

$$\lambda = \frac{1.0 \times 10^{-3} \text{ m} \times 7.1 \times 10^{-4} \text{ m}}{1.20 \text{ m}}$$

$= 5.92 \times 10^{-7}$ m.

3.13 Use the largest convenient value of D (e.g. 40 mm), and measure x for the central fringe. For the direct measurement of λ, find the length of a wavetrain of 8 or 9 ripples.

3.14 (a) Let the fringe spacings for the blue and yellow light be x_b and x_y respectively.

$$x_b = \frac{4.5 \times 10^{-7} \times 2}{5 \times 10^{-4}} = 1.8 \times 10^{-3} \text{ mm}$$

$$x_y = \frac{6.0 \times 10^{-7} \times 2}{5 \times 10^{-4}} = 2.4 \times 10^{-3} \text{ mm}$$

(b) See figure 3.15a.
(c) See figure 3.15b. There will be intense blackening, corresponding to a bright fringe, every 7.2 mm.

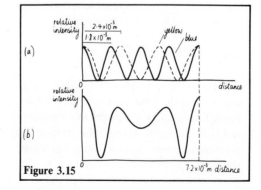

Figure 3.15

3.15 (a) and (b) See figure 3.16.
(c) At O. The path difference is zero here and constructive superposition occurs for all wavelengths.
(d) White central fringe with red edges.
(e) The first order fringe is white with a blue edge near the centre O and a red edge away from O. The central fringe is symmetrical, the other fringes are not. The first order fringes have lower maximum intensity, and are wider than the central fringe because the patterns due to different colours are becoming more out of step.
(f) There is no region of minimum between the first and second order fringes.
(g) About five fringes can be observed (the central figure plus two on each side) before the various fringe patterns get so much out of step that maxima and minima cannot be observed and uniform whiteness results.

3.16 (a) The pattern will be displaced in the opposite direction (that is, the zero order central fringe will move below O).
(b) The pattern will be displaced along the screen in the same direction (central fringe moving up).
(c) If S moves towards the slits the fringe pattern may appear brighter as more light passes through the slits S_1 and S_2.
The pattern could disappear if S is so near that light does not spread out (diffract) enough to pass through the slits.

3.17 (a) $\theta = (n - 1) A$.
(b) A, n and l.
(c) For small angles, $d/2 = l\theta$, so $d = 2l\theta = 2l(n - 1)A$, where A is in radians.
(d) $d = 0.2 (1.50 - 1) 8.7 \times 10^{-3}$ m
$= 8.7 \times 10^{-4}$ m
(e) Separation $= \lambda D/d$
$$= \frac{5 \times 10^{-7} \times 0.90}{8.7 \times 10^{-4}} \text{ m}$$
$= 5.2 \times 10^{-4}$ m.
(f) Halve the distance D or double the distance l.

3.19 (a) 2.2×10^8 m s^{-1}.
(b) 2.99×10^8 m s^{-1}.

3.21 (a) 3.0 m.
(b) ± 3.0 m in the total path, ± 1.5 m in the moon's distance from earth.
(c) Error $= 3 \times 10^{-4} \times 8 \times 10^3$ m for each transit of the atmosphere.
Total error $= +4.8$ m, which gives a value for the calculated distance which is too large.
Yes, the error is significant, being three times as big as the limiting uncertainty due to the timing method.

Chapter 4

4.1 (a) A ray is a normal to a wavefront or a line indicating the direction of travel of the wave energy.
(b) A beam indicates the space through which wave energy is flowing. In a converging beam the cross-section of the wavefront becomes smaller as the wave moves.
(c) Two rays crossing represent two waves crossing, and by the principle of superposition this occurs without the waves affecting each other.

4.3 The refractive index of a material depends on the frequency (colour) of the light. The speed of blue light in a medium is less than the speed of red light, so blue light is refracted more than red light. Therefore the refractive index of the medium is greater for blue light than for red light.

4.5 (a) It will be refracted away from the normal, since it is travelling from a dense to a less dense medium.
(b) Angle of refraction in water $= 59.5°$.
Using $n_1 \sin i_1 = n_2 \sin i_2$,
$1.50 \times \sin 50° = 1.33 \times \sin i_2$,
where i_2 is the angle of refraction in water.
Therefore $\sin i_2 = \dfrac{1.50}{1.33} \times \sin 50°$,
and $i_2 = 59.5°$.

4.7 Refractive index of turpentine $= 1.48$.
Using $n = \dfrac{\text{real depth}}{\text{apparent depth}}$,
$n = \dfrac{4.00 \text{ cm}}{2.70 \text{ cm}} = 1.48$.

4.9 (a) The angle of refraction increases.
(b) The maximum value of the angle of refraction is 90°.

4.10 (a) $n_2 \sin c = n_1 \sin 90°$, and since $\sin 90° = 1$, $n_1/n_2 = \sin c$, or $n_2/n_1 = 1/\sin c$.
(b) $c = 41.8°$.
If $n_a = 1$, $1.50 \times \sin c = 1 \times \sin 90°$.
Therefore $\sin c = 0.67$, and $c = 41.8°$.
(c) The light must be travelling from a dense to a less dense medium. The angle of incidence in the denser medium must be greater than the critical angle.
(d) The angle of refraction seems to have a sine greater than unity, which is impossible. Mathematical impossibility corresponds to physical non-existence.

4.12 (a) For refraction at P,
$n_a \sin 90° = n_g \sin c$.
For refraction at Q,
$n_g \sin (90° - c) = n_a \sin \theta$,
but $\sin (90° - c) = \cos c$,
so $n_g \cos c = n_a \sin \theta$.
Dividing this equation by the first one,
$\dfrac{\cos c}{\sin c} = \dfrac{\sin \theta}{1}$, so $\sin \theta = 1/\tan c$.
(b) The greatest value that the refractive index may have is 1.41.
The critical angle c has a minimum value when the light leaves AD at grazing emergence ($\theta = 90°$). Then $\tan c = 1$, and $c = 45°$. The maximum value of refractive index is given by $n_g/n_a = 1/\sin 45°$, so $n_g = 1.41$.
(c) The light will emerge from face DC after total internal reflection at face AD. This will occur for all rays for which total internal reflection occurs at face AD.

4.14 (a) The angle of deviation decreases to a minimum value and then increases.
(b) At small angles of incidence the light is totally internally reflected at the second face of the prism, since the angle of incidence with the second face is greater than the critical angle.

4.15 From figure 4.6c, $A = 2i_g$. If i_g is greater than the critical angle, the light will be totally internally reflected, therefore must be less than twice the critical angle.